Literary Heritage

Advisory Editorial Board
Dora V. Smith
Joseph Mersand
James Squire

Short Stories II

ELIZABETH SCHELD

Chairman, Department of English
Los Angeles High School
Los Angeles, California

New York **THE MACMILLAN COMPANY**

Vocabulary studies on pages 22, 23, 60, 61, 102, 103, 131, 132, 138, 139, etc., are reprinted from *A Book of Stories*, by Brother H. Raphael, F.S.C. © 1960 by The Macmillan Company.

ACKNOWLEDGMENTS

For permission to use material in this book, grateful acknowledgment is made to the following:

Mr. Isaac Asimov: For "The Feeling of Power," by Isaac Asimov. Copyright 1957, by Quinn Publishing Co., Inc.

Brandt & Brandt: For "The Sea Devil," by Arthur Gordon. First published in *The Saturday Evening Post*. Copyright 1953 by The Curtis Publishing Company. For "One Ordinary Day, With Peanuts," by Shirley Jackson. First published in *The Magazine of Fantasy and Science Fiction*. Copyright 1954 by Fantasy House, Inc. For "By the Waters of Babylon," by Stephen Vincent Benét, from *Selected Works of Stephen Vincent Benét*, Holt, Rinehart & Winston, Inc. Copyright 1937, by Stephen Vincent Benét.

Curtis Brown, Ltd.: For "Susana and the Shepherd," by Margaret Craven. Reprinted by permission of the author; © 1956 by The Curtis Publishing Company.

Jonathan Cape, Ltd.: For "The Sniper," from *Spring Sowing*, by Liam O'Flaherty.

Esquire, Inc.: For "The Tiger's Heart," by Jim Kjelgaard. Reprinted from *Esquire*, April 1951; © 1951 by Esquire, Inc.

Estate of Johan Bojer: For "Fishermen," by Johan Bojer. Copyright 1924 by John Bojer; Copyright renewed, 1951, by Johan Bojer.

Harcourt, Brace and Company, Inc.: For "Road to the Isles," by Jessamyn West. Copyright, 1948, by Jessamyn West. Originally published in *The New Yorker* and now included in *Cress Delahanty* by Jessamyn West. For "The Parsley Garden," by William Saroyan, from *The Assyrian and Other Stories* by William Saroyan. For "The Sniper," from *Spring Sowing*, by Liam O'Flaherty. All reprinted by permission of Harcourt, Brace & World, Inc.

A. M. Heath & Company, Ltd.: For "Road to the Isles," by Jessamyn West, from *Cress Delahanty*.

Harold Matson Company: For "Luke Baldwin's Vow," by Morley Callaghan. Copyright 1947 by The Curtis Publishing Company.

The New Yorker: For "The Secret Life of Walter Mitty," by James Thurber.

The Macmillan Company, New York
Brett-Macmillan, Ltd., Galt, Ontario
Printed in the United States of America

8B

ACKNOWLEDGMENTS (*Continued*)

Harold Ober Associates, Incorporated: For "Water Never Hurt a Man," by Walter D. Edmonds. Copyright © 1930, 1934, by Walter D. Edmonds.

Laurence Pollinger Limited: For "The Parsley Garden," by William Saroyan, from *The Assyrian and Other Stories*.

Random House, Inc., and Chatto & Windus Ltd.: For "Two Soldiers," by William Faulkner, from *Collected Stories of William Faulkner*. Copyright 1942 by The Curtis Publishing Company.

Mr. Jesse Stuart: For "Spring Victory," by Jesse Stuart, from *Tales From the Plum Grove Hills*.

The Viking Press, Inc., and McIntosh and Otis, Inc.: For "Molly Morgan," from *The Pastures of Heaven* by John Steinbeck. Copyright 1932 by John Steinbeck.

Contents

Short Stories II

Reading the Short Story

You have been reading, hearing, and telling stories all of your life. Some have been fanciful; some have been true. Some have been simple anecdotes, and others have been artfully contrived. Perhaps most of the time you have read and listened as a spectator, releasing yourself to the enchantment of the storyteller. Now, in this volume, you will read short stories that are the products of skilled literary artists. You will read for pleasure, but you will want to read thoughtfully, for thoughtful reading will double your pleasure. You will enjoy the writer's magic, but you will want to get behind the performance to see how the magic works.

First of all, a story must be entertainment. As an entertainment, it must interest and divert you. That is, the story must capture your attention so completely that you will shut out the world around you and, momentarily, even your own affairs. The stories in this book can do this if you give them a chance. Arrange to read them without interruption, and in reasonably quiet surroundings.

A story is entertainment, but it is a special kind of entertainment, for it requires the participation of the reader. A good reader does not simply let the story happen to him. He gets into the story and reads with his eyes and ears open. He reads with his mind *and* his heart. A good reading is a *re-creation* in which the reader works alongside the writer.

You will read, then, with both your mind and your heart. You will react emotionally to the characters and what happens to them. You will also react thoughtfully to them. Most stories have a point to make. The writer is not simply describing a series of occurrences; he is telling you, sometimes directly, and sometimes in very subtle ways, what these occurrences mean.

You must not expect every story to have a happy ending. If you are ready to face up to the facts of life—and you are—you can face up to the facts of fiction. You will read with equal enjoyment stories that end happily and stories that end tragically.

It is important to remember that a short story is a work of fiction and not a reporter's account of actual events. If the story seems very real, it is because the writer has been very skillful in putting it together. The writer's skill is something to keep in mind. The stories in this book were not put together haphazardly. The characters do not say just anything or everything that comes into their minds. Incidents are not put down in just any order. Outcomes are not a matter of chance. They are made reasonable and believable by clues and foreshadowing. Circumstances, which, at first reading, may seem trivial, later assume major importance. It is the writer's art that makes this so.

Good short stories are constructed with the greatest care. For full pleasure they should be read with care. You will discover that the stories in this book bear thinking about, and that the thinking about them is a source of pleasure.

The Sea Devil

ARTHUR GORDON

When a man casts a net into the sea, he must not be surprised at what he brings up.

THE man came out of the house and stood quite still, listening. Behind him, the lights glowed in the cheerful room, the books were neat and orderly in their cases, the radio talked importantly to itself. In front of him, the bay stretched dark and silent, one of the countless lagoons that border the coast where Florida thrusts its great green thumb deep into the tropics.

It was late in September. The night was breathless; summer's dead hand still lay heavy on the land. The man moved forward six paces and stood on the sea wall. He dropped his cigarette and noted where the tiny spark hissed and went out. The tide was beginning to ebb.

Somewhere out in the blackness a mullet jumped and fell back with a sullen splash. Heavy with roe, they were jumping less often, now. They would not take a hook, but a practiced eye could see the swirls they made in the glassy water. In the dark of the moon, a skilled man with a cast net might take half a dozen in an hour's work. And a big mullet makes a meal for a family.

The man turned abruptly and went into the garage, where his cast net hung. He was in his late twenties, wide-shouldered and strong. He did not have to fish for a living, or even for food. He was a man who worked with his head, not with his hands. But he liked to go casting alone at night.

He liked the loneliness and the labor of it. He liked the clean taste of salt when he gripped the edge of the net with his teeth as a cast netter must. He liked the arching flight of sixteen pounds of lead and linen against the starlight, and the weltering crash of the net into the unsuspecting water. He liked the harsh tug of the retrieving rope

3

around his wrist, and the way the net came alive when the cast was true, and the thud of captured fish on the floor boards of the skiff.

He liked all that because he found in it a reality that seemed to be missing from his twentieth-century job and from his daily life. He liked being the hunter, skilled and solitary and elemental. There was no conscious cruelty in the way he felt. It was the way things had been in the beginning.

The man lifted the net down carefully and lowered it into a bucket. He put a paddle beside the bucket. Then he went into the house. When he came out, he was wearing swimming trunks and a pair of old tennis shoes. Nothing else.

The skiff, flat-bottomed, was moored off the sea wall. He would not go far, he told himself. Just to the tumbledown dock half a mile away. Mullet had a way of feeding around old pilings after dark. If he moved quietly, he might pick up two or three in one cast close to the dock. And maybe a couple of others on the way down or back.

He shoved off and stood motionless for a moment, letting his eyes grow accustomed to the dark. Somewhere out in the channel a porpoise blew with a sound like steam escaping. The man smiled a little; porpoises were his friends. Once, fishing in the Gulf he had seen the charter-boat captain reach overside and gaff a baby porpoise through the sinewy part of the tail. He had hoisted it aboard, had dropped it into the bait well, where it thrashed around, puzzled and unhappy. And the mother had swum alongside the boat and under the boat and around the boat, nudging the stout planking with her back, slapping it with her tail, until the man felt sorry for her and made the captain let the baby porpoise go.

He took the net from the bucket, slipped the noose in the retrieving rope over his wrist, pulled the slipknot tight. It was an old net, but still serviceable; he had rewoven the rents made by underwater snags. He coiled the thirty-foot rope carefully, making sure there were no kinks. A tangled rope, he knew, would spoil any cast.

The basic design of the net had not changed in three thousand years. It was a mesh circle with a diameter of fourteen feet. It measured close to fifteen yards around the circumference and could, if thrown perfectly, blanket a hundred and fifty square feet of sea water. In the center of this radial trap was a small iron collar where the retrieving rope met the twenty-three separate drawstrings leading to the outer rim of the net. Along this rim, spaced an inch and a half apart, were the heavy lead sinkers.

The man raised the iron collar until it was a foot above his head. The net hung soft and pliant and deadly. He shook it gently, making sure that the drawstrings were not tangled, that the sinkers were hanging true. Then he eased it down and picked up the paddle.

The night was black as a witch's cat; the stars looked fuzzy and dim. Down to the southward, the lights of a causeway made a yellow necklace across the sky. To the man's left were the tangled roots of a mangrove swamp; to his right, the open waters of the bay. Most of it was fairly shallow, but there were channels eight feet deep. The man could not see the old dock, but he knew where it was. He pulled the paddle quietly through the water, and the phosphorescence glowed and died.

For five minutes he paddled. Then, twenty feet ahead of the skiff, a mullet jumped. A big fish, close to three pounds. For a moment it hung in the still air, gleaming dully. Then it vanished. But the ripples marked the spot, and where there was one there were often others.

The man stood up quickly. He picked up the coiled rope, and with the same hand grasped the net at a point four feet below the iron collar. He raised the skirt to his mouth, gripped it strongly with his teeth. He slid his free hand as far as it would go down the circumference of the net so that he had three points of contact with the mass of cordage and metal. He made sure his feet were planted solidly. Then he waited, feeling the tension that is older than the human race, the fierce exhilaration of the hunter at the moment of ambush, the atavistic desire to capture and kill and ultimately consume.

A mullet swirled, ahead and to the left. The man swung the heavy net back, twisting his body and bending his knees so as to get more upward thrust. He shot it forward, letting go simultaneously with rope hand and with teeth, holding a fraction of a second longer with the other hand so as to give the net the necessary spin, impart the centrifugal force that would make it flare into a circle. The skiff ducked sideways, but he kept his balance. The net fell with a splash.

The man waited for five seconds. Then he began to retrieve it, pulling in a series of sharp jerks so that the drawstrings would gather the net inward, like a giant fist closing on this segment of the teeming sea. He felt the net quiver, and knew it was not empty. He swung it, dripping, over the gunwhale, saw the broad silver side of the mullet quivering, saw too the gleam of a smaller fish. He looked closely to make sure no sting ray was hidden in the mesh, then raised the iron collar and shook the net out. The mullet fell with a thud and flapped wildly. The other victim was an angel fish, beautifully marked, but too small to keep. The man picked it up gently and dropped it overboard. He coiled the rope, took up the paddle. He would cast no more until he came to the dock.

The skiff moved on. At last, ten feet apart, a pair of stakes rose up gauntly out of the night. Barnacle encrusted, they once had marked the approach from the main channel. The man guided the skiff between them, then put the paddle down softly. He stood up, reached for the net, tightened the noose around his wrist. From here he could drift down upon the dock. He could see it now, a ruined skeleton in the starshine. Beyond it a mullet jumped and fell back with a flat, liquid sound. The man raised the edge of the net, put it between his teeth. He would not cast at a single swirl, he decided; he would wait until he saw two or three close together. The skiff was barely moving. He felt his muscles tense themselves, awaiting the signal from the brain.

Behind him in the channel he heard the porpoise blow again, nearer now. He frowned in the darkness. If the porpoise chose to fish this area, the mullet would scatter and vanish. There was no time to lose.

A school of sardines surfaced suddenly, skittering along like drops of mercury. Something, perhaps the shadow of the skiff, had frightened them. The old dock loomed very close. A mullet broke water just too far away; then another, nearer. The man marked the spreading ripples and decided to wait no longer.

He swung back the net, heavier now that it was wet. He had to turn his head, but out of the corner of his eye he saw two swirls in the back water just off the starboard bow. They were about eight feet apart, and they had the sluggish oily look that marks the presence of something big just below the surface. His conscious mind had no time to function, but instinct told him that the net was wide enough to cover both swirls if he could alter the direction of his cast. He could not halt the swing, but he shifted his feet slightly and made the cast off balance. He saw the net shoot forward, flare into an oval, and drop just where he wanted it.

Then the sea exploded in his face. In a frenzy of spray, a great horned thing shot like a huge bat out of the water. The man saw the mesh of his net etched against the mottled blackness of its body and he knew, in the split second in which thought was still possible, that those twin swirls had been made not by two mullet, but by the wing tips of the giant ray of the Gulf Coast, *Manta birostris*, also known as clam cracker, devil ray, sea devil.

The man gave a hoarse cry. He tried to claw the slipknot off his wrist, but there was no time. The quarter-inch line snapped taut. He shot over the side of the skiff as if he had roped a runaway locomotive. He hit the water head first and seemed to bounce once. He plowed a blinding furrow for perhaps ten yards. Then the line went slack as the sea devil jumped again. It was not the full-grown manta of the deep Gulf, but it was close to nine feet from tip to tip and it weighed over a thousand pounds. Up into the air it went, pearl-colored underbelly gleaming as it twisted in a frantic effort to dislodge the clinging thing that had fallen upon it. Up into the starlight, a monstrous survival from the dawn of time.

The water was less than four feet deep. Sobbing and choking, the man struggled for a foothold on the slimy bottom. Sucking in great gulps of air, he fought to free himself from the rope. But the slipknot was jammed deep into his wrist; he might as well have tried to loosen a circle of steel.

The ray came down with a thunderous splash and drove forward again. The flexible net followed every movement, impeding it hardly at all. The man weighed a hundred and seventy-five pounds, and he was braced for the shock, and he had the desperate strength that comes from looking into the blank eyes of death. It was useless. His arm straightened out with a jerk that seemed to dislocate his shoulder; his feet shot out from under him; his head went under again. Now at last he knew how the fish must feel when the line tightens and drags him toward the alien element that is his doom. Now he knew.

Desperately he dug the fingers of his free hand into the ooze, felt them dredge a futile channel through broken shells and the ribbon-like sea grasses. He tried to raise his head, but could not get it clear. Torrents of spray choked him as the ray plunged toward deep water.

His eyes were of no use to him in the foam-streaked blackness. He closed them tight, and at once an insane sequence of pictures flashed through his mind. He saw his wife sitting in their living room, reading, waiting calmly for his return. He saw the mullet he had just caught, gasping its life away on the floor boards of the skiff. He saw the cigarette he had flung from the sea wall touch the water and expire with a tiny hiss. He saw all these things and many others simultaneously in his mind as his body fought silently and tenaciously for its existence. His hand touched something hard and closed on it in a death grip, but it was only the sharp-edged helmet of a horseshoe crab, and after an instant he let it go.

He had been under the water perhaps fifteen seconds now, and something in his brain told him quite calmly that he could last another forty or fifty and then the red flashes behind his eyes would merge into darkness, and the water would pour into his lungs in one sharp painful shock, and he would be finished.

This thought spurred him to a desperate effort. He reached up and caught his pinioned wrist with his free hand. He doubled up his knees to create more drag. He thrashed his body madly, like a fighting fish, from side to side. This did not disturb the ray, but now one of the great wings tore through the mesh, and the net slipped lower over the fins projecting like horns from below the nightmare head, and the sea devil jumped again.

And once more the man was able to get his feet on the bottom and his head above water, and he saw ahead of him the pair of ancient stakes that marked the approach to the channel. He knew that if he was dragged much beyond those stakes he would be in eight feet of water, and the ray would go down to hug the bottom as rays always do, and then no power on earth could save him. So in the moment of respite that was granted him, he flung himself toward them. For a moment he thought his captor yielded a bit. Then the ray moved off again, but more slowly now, and for a few yards the man was able to keep his feet on the bottom. Twice he hurled himself back against the rope with all his strength, hoping that something would break. But nothing broke. The mesh of the net was ripped and torn, but the draw lines were strong, and the stout perimeter cord threaded through the sinkers was even stronger.

The man could feel nothing now in his trapped hand, it was numb; but the ray could feel the powerful lunges of the unknown thing that was trying to restrain it. It drove its great wings against the unyielding water and forged ahead, dragging the man and pushing a sullen wave in front of it.

The man had swung as far as he could toward the stakes. He plunged toward one and missed it by inches. His feet slipped and he went down on his knees. Then the ray swerved sharply and the second stake came right at him. He reached out with his free hand and caught it.

He caught it just above the surface, six or eight inches below high-water mark. He felt the razor-sharp barnacles bite into his hand, collapse under the pressure, drive their tiny slime-covered shell splinters deep into his flesh. He felt the pain, and he welcomed it, and he made his fingers into an iron claw that would hold until the tendons were severed or the skin was shredded from the bone. The ray felt the pressure increase with a jerk that stopped it dead in the water. For a moment all was still as the tremendous forces came into equilibrium.

Then the net slipped again, and the perimeter cord came down over the sea devil's eyes, blinding it momentarily. The great ray settled to the bottom and braced its wings against the mud and hurled itself forward and upward.

The stake was only a four-by-four of creosoted pine, and it was old. Ten thousand tides had swirled around it. Worms had bored; parasites had clung. Under the crust of barnacles it still had some heart left, but not enough. The man's grip was five feet above the floor of the bay; the leverage was too great. The stake snapped off at its base.

The ray lunged forward, dragging the man and the useless timber. The man had his lungs full of air, but when the stake snapped he thought of expelling the air and inhaling the water so as to have it finished quickly. He thought of this, but he did not do it. And then, just at the channel's edge, the ray met the porpoise coming in.

The porpoise had fed well this night and was in no hurry, but it was a methodical creature and it intended to make a sweep around the old dock before the tide dropped too low. It had no quarrel with any ray, but it feared no fish in the sea, and when the great black shadow came rushing blindly and unavoidably, it rolled fast and struck once with its massive horizontal tail.

The blow descended on the ray's flat body with a sound like a pistol shot. It would have broken a buffalo's back, and even the sea devil was half stunned. It veered wildly and turned back toward shallow water. It passed within ten feet of the man, face down in the water. It slowed and almost stopped, wing tips moving faintly, gathering strength for another rush.

The man had heard the tremendous slap of the great mammal's tail and the snorting gasp as it plunged away. He felt the line go slack again, and he raised his dripping face, and he reached for the bottom with his feet. He found it, but now the water was up to his neck. He plucked at the noose once more with his lacerated hand, but there was no strength in his fingers. He felt the tension come back into the line as the ray began to move again, and for half a second he was tempted to throw himself backward and fight as he had been doing, pitting his strength against the vastly superior strength of the brute.

But the acceptance of imminent death had done something to his brain. It had driven out the fear, and with the fear had gone the panic. He could think now, and he knew with absolute certainty that if he was to make any use of this last chance that had been given him, it would have to be based on the one faculty that had carried man to his pre-eminence above all beasts, the faculty of reason. Only by using his brain could he possibly survive, and he called on his brain for a solution, and his brain responded. It offered him one.

He did not know whether his body still had the strength to carry out the brain's commands, but he began to swim forward, toward the ray that was still moving hesitantly away from the channel. He swam forward, feeling the rope go slack as he gained on the creature.

Ahead of him he saw the one remaining stake, and he made himself swim faster until he was parallel with the ray and the rope trailed behind both of them in a deep U. He swam with a surge of desperate energy that came from nowhere so that he was slightly in the lead as they came to the stake. He passed on one side of it; the ray was on the other.

Then the man took one last deep breath, and he went down under the black water until he was sitting on the bottom of the bay. He put one foot over the line so that it passed under his bent knee. He drove both his heels into the mud, and he clutched the slimy grass with his bleeding hand, and he waited for the tension to come again.

The ray passed on the other side of the stake, moving faster now. The rope grew taut again, and it began to drag the man back toward the stake. He held his prisoned wrist close to the bottom, under his knee, and he prayed that the stake would not break. He felt the rope vibrate as the barnacles bit into it. He did not know whether the rope would crush the barnacles or whether the barnacles would cut the rope. All he knew was that in five seconds or less he would be dragged into the stake and cut to ribbons if he tried to hold on; or drowned if he didn't.

He felt himself sliding slowly, and then faster, and suddenly the ray made a great leap forward, and the rope burned around the base of the stake, and the man's foot hit it hard. He kicked himself backward with his remaining strength, and the rope parted and he was free.

He came slowly to the surface.

Thirty feet away the sea devil made one tremendous leap and disappeared into the darkness. The man raised his wrist and looked at the frayed length of rope dangling from it. Twenty inches, perhaps. He lifted his other hand and felt the hot blood start instantly, but he didn't care. He put this hand on the stake above the barnacles and held on to the good, rough, honest wood. He heard a strange noise, and realized that it was himself, sobbing.

High above, there was a droning sound, and looking up he saw the nightly plane from New Orleans inbound for Tampa. Calm and serene, it sailed, symbol of man's proud mastery over nature. Its lights winked red and green for a moment; then it was gone.

Slowly, painfully, the man began to move through the placid water. He came to the skiff at last and climbed into it. The mullet, still alive, slapped convulsively with its tail. The man reached down with his torn hand, picked up the mullet, let it go.

He began to work on the slip-knot doggedly with his teeth. His mind was almost a blank, but not quite. He knew one thing. He knew he would do no more casting alone at night. Not in the dark of the moon. No, not he.

Questions for discussion

1. How did the man in the story get into trouble? Was it by making mistakes? By breaking the law? By being careless? Was it something else?
2. Did the porpoise save the man's life? Support your answer by referring to the story.
3. What was the man struggling to do? What was the giant ray strug-

gling to do? Were the man and the ray fighting each other? If so, who do you believe won the fight?

4. "But the acceptance of imminent death had done something to his brain." What does this sentence mean? What has happened to the man's brain?

5. "The man raised his wrist and looked at the frayed length of rope— Twenty inches perhaps." What is the significance of "Twenty inches perhaps."?

6. How did the man react to his release from danger? Why did he put his hand on the stake (p. 11)? Why does the writer refer to the stake as "the good rough honest wood"?

7. Why did the man throw the mullet back into the water at the close of the story? Has he decided not to do any more fishing in the future?

8. The theme of a story is its central idea—what the story is about. What is the theme of "The Sea Devil"? In order to discover the theme of this story, first recall the answers to questions 1 and 3 above, and then reread the paragraph that begins, "But the acceptance of imminent death . . ." Why is the man in the story given no name?

9. Why does the writer introduce the paragraph about the airplane at the close of the story? Earlier (p. 7), there is a paragraph about an "insane sequence of pictures" that flashed through the man's mind. What is the effect of this paragraph?

10. There is a kind of justice in the help that is given to the man by the porpoise. Why? What other experience had the man had with porpoises?

11. In most stories, there is a struggle or conflict that has to be settled. The story is satisfying only if the struggle is settled in terms which the reader finds believable. If coincidence or chance settles the struggle, the story is hard to believe and not satisfying. In "The Sea Devil," is the action of the porpoise believable? Is its appearance a matter of chance? How has the author prepared the reader for the appearance of the porpoise?

12. POINT OF VIEW. A writer may tell a story objectively, putting down only those details that an outside observer would see in the situation. That is one point of view. The writer may also tell his story from the point of view of one of the characters in his story. Finally, he may take an "omniscient" point of view. That is, he may decide to tell what is going on in the minds of several of his characters even though they are miles apart. The *point of view* is the outlook of the observer who tells the story.

"The Sea Devil" is written from the point of view of an outside observer who might have seen the entire action from a boat nearby. In two spots, however, this point of view is changed. It is changed when the writer tells what passed through the man's mind. It is changed again in the paragraph on page 9 that begins, "The porpoise had fed well . . ." In what way does this paragraph change the point of view?

Vocabulary growth

VARIANT MEANINGS. Many words in common use have special and unusual meanings. One such word is *ray*, which in "The Sea Devil" refers to a fish. Another is the word *true*. On page 3 you read, "He liked the harsh tug of the retrieving rope around his wrist, and the way the net came alive when the cast was *true* . . ." Can you figure out from the context of the sentence what the word *true* means as it is used here?

IMAGES. Words that appeal to the senses arouse pictures or images in the reader's mind. "The Sea Devil" is rich in its use of such words. For example, in the first page of the story the writer speaks of *"glassy water," "Clean taste* of salt," *"harsh* tug of the retrieving rope." Look through the story again and pick out other examples of image-words.

FIGURES OF SPEECH. A figure of speech is a way of making a comparison. In some figures of speech, "like" and "as" appear. For example, ". . . a porpoise blew with a sound *like* steam escaping." In other figures, *like* does not appear, and one thing is spoken of as if it were another: ". . . Florida thrusts *its great green thumb* into the tropics." Florida does not have a thumb, but on the map it looks like a thumb. There is another example on the first page of the story: ". . . summer's *dead hand* still lay heavy on the land." Find other figures of speech in the story.

For composition

1. Write a brief account of the man's arrival at the house. Write it from the wife's point of view, and use dialogue. You might begin:

   "My husband had been out longer than usual, but it did not occur to me to worry, because he is very skillful with boats and fishing equipment. I had just turned off the radio, when I heard a strange noise, like someone crying . . ."

2. Assume that a newspaper reporter called the next morning. Write an account of the interview. If you prefer, write the news story that the reporter turned in. Your headline:

   "Local Man Cheats Death in Battle with Giant Ray"

3. The man in the story is very skillfully portrayed even though he is given no name. Make a list of his personality traits and characteristics. Give him a name and write a character sketch of him.

A Retrieved Reformation

O. HENRY

What made Jimmy Valentine lay aside his safe-cracking tools? What made him take them up again? Can a criminal of long experience every really reform?

A guard came to the prison shoe shop, where Jimmy Valentine was assiduously stitching uppers, and escorted him to the front office. There the warden handed Jimmy his pardon, which had been signed that morning by the governor. Jimmy took it in a tired kind of way. He had served nearly ten months of a four-year sentence. He had expected to stay only about three months, at the longest. When a man with as many friends on the outside as Jimmy Valentine had is received in the "stir," it is hardly worth while to cut his hair.

"Now, Valentine," said the warden, "you'll go out in the morning. Brace up, and make a man of yourself. You're not a bad fellow at heart. Stop cracking safes, and live straight."

"Me?" said Jimmy, in surprise. "Why, I never cracked a safe in my life."

"Oh, no," laughed the warden. "Of course not. Let's see, now. How was it you happened to get sent up on that Springfield job? Was it because you wouldn't prove an alibi for fear of compromising somebody in extremely high-toned society? Or was it simply a case of a mean old jury that had it in for you? It's always one or the other with you innocent victims."

"Me?" said Jimmy, still blankly virtuous. "Why, warden, I never was in Springfield in my life!"

"Take him back, Cronin," smiled the warden, "and fix him up with outgoing clothes. Unlock him at seven in the morning, and let him come to the bull-pen. Better think over my advice, Valentine."

At a quarter past seven on the next morning Jimmy stood in the warden's outer office. He had on a suit of the villainously fitting, ready-made clothes and a pair of the stiff, squeaky shoes that the state furnishes to its discharged compulsory guests.

The clerk handed him a railroad ticket and the five-dollar bill with which the law expects him to rehabilitate himself into good citizenship and prosperity. The warden gave him a cigar, and shook hands. Valentine, 9762, was chronicled on the books "Pardoned by Governor," and Mr. James Valentine walked out into the sunshine.

Disregarding the song of the birds, the waving green trees, and the smell of the flowers, Jimmy headed straight for a restaurant. There he tasted the first sweet joys of liberty in the shape of a broiled chicken and a bottle of white wine—followed by a cigar a grade better than the one the warden had given him. From there he proceeded leisurely to the depot. He tossed a quarter into the hat of a blind man sitting by the door, and boarded his train. Three hours set him down in a little town near the state line. He went to the café of one Mike Dolan and shook hands with Mike, who was alone behind the bar.

"Sorry we couldn't make it sooner, Jimmy, me boy," said Mike. "But we had that protest from Springfield to buck against, and the governor nearly balked. Feeling all right?"

"Fine," said Jimmy. "Got my key?"

He got his key and went upstairs, unlocking the door of a room at the rear. Everything was just as he had left it. There on the floor was still Ben Price's collar-button that had been torn from that eminent detective's shirt-band when they had overpowered Jimmy to arrest him.

Pulling out from the wall a folding bed, Jimmy slid back a panel in the wall and dragged out a dust-covered suitcase. He opened this and gazed fondly at the finest set of burglar's tools in the East. It was a complete set, made of specially tempered steel, the latest designs in drills, punches, braces and bits, jimmies, clamps, and augers, with two or three novelties, invented by Jimmy himself, in which he took pride. Over nine hundred dollars they had cost him to have made at ——, a place where they made such things for the profession.

In half an hour Jimmy went downstairs and through the café. He was now dressed in tasteful and well-fitting clothes, and carried his dusted and cleaned suitcase in hand.

"Got anything on?" asked Mike Dolan genially.

"Me?" said Jimmy, in a puzzled tone. "I don't understand. I'm representing the New York Amalgamated Short Snap Biscuit Cracker and Frazzled Wheat Company."

This statement delighted Mike to such an extent that Jimmy had to take a seltzer-and-milk on the spot. He never touched "hard" drinks.

A week after the release of Valentine, 9762, there was a neat job of safe-burglary done in Richmond, Indiana, with no clue to the author. A scant eight hundred dollars was all that was secured. Two weeks after that a patented, improved, burglar-proof safe in Logansport was opened like a cheese to the tune of fifteen hundred dollars, currency; securities and silver untouched. That began to interest the rogue-catchers. Then an old-fashioned bank-safe in Jefferson City became active and threw out of its crater an eruption of bank notes amounting to five thousand dollars. The losses were now high enough to bring the matter up into Ben Price's class of work. By comparing notes, a remarkable similarity in the methods of the burglaries was noticed. Ben Price investigated the scenes of the robberies, and was heard to remark:

"That's Dandy Jim Valentine's autograph. He's resumed business. Look at that combination knob—jerked out as easy as pulling up a radish in wet weather. He's got the only clamps that can do it. And look how clean those tumblers were punched out! Jimmy never has to drill but one hole. Yes, I guess I want Mr. Valentine. He'll do his bit next time without any short-time or clemency foolishness."

Ben Price knew Jimmy's habits. He had learned them while working up the Springfield Case. Long jumps, quick getaways, no confederates, and a taste for good society—these ways had helped Mr. Valentine to become noted as a successful dodger of retribution. It was given out that Ben Price had taken up the trail of the elusive cracksman, and other people with burglar-proof safes felt more at ease.

One afternoon Jimmy Valentine and his suitcase climbed out of the mail-hack in Elmore, a little town five miles off the railroad down in the black-jack country of Arkansas. Jimmy, looking like an athletic young senior just home from college, went down the board sidewalk toward the hotel.

A young lady crossed the street, passed him at the corner, and entered a door over which was the sign "The Elmore Bank." Jimmy Valentine looked into her eyes, forgot what he was, and became another man. She lowered her eyes and colored slightly. Young men of Jimmy's style and looks were scarce in Elmore.

Jimmy collared a boy that was loafing on the steps of the bank as if he were one of the stockholders, and began to ask him questions about the town, feeding him dimes at intervals. By and by the young lady came out, looking royally unconscious of the young man with the suitcase, and went her way.

"Isn't that young lady Miss Polly Simpson?" asked Jimmy.

"Naw," said the boy. "She's Annabel Adams. Her pa owns this bank. What'd you come to Elmore for? Is that a gold watch-chain? I'm going to get a bulldog. Got any more dimes?"

Jimmy went to the Planter's Hotel, registered as Ralph D. Spencer, and engaged a room. He leaned on the desk and declared his platform to the clerk. He said he had come to Elmore to look for a location to go into business. How was the shoe business, now, in the town? He had thought of the shoe business. Was there an opening?

The clerk was impressed by the clothes and manner of Jimmy. He, himself, was something of a pattern of fashion to the thinly gilded youth of Elmore, but he now perceived his shortcomings. While trying to figure out Jimmy's manner of tying his four-in-hand he cordially gave information.

Yes, there ought to be a good opening in the shoe line. There wasn't an exclusive shoe-store in the place. The drygoods and the general stores handled them. Business in all lines was fairly good. Hoped Mr. Spencer would decide to locate in Elmore. He would find it a pleasant town to live in, and the people very sociable.

Mr. Spencer thought he would stop over in the town a few days and look over the situation. No, the clerk needn't call the boy. He would carry up his suitcase himself; it was rather heavy.

Mr. Ralph Spencer, the phoenix that arose from Jimmy Valentine's ashes—ashes left by the flame of a sudden and transforming attack of love—remained in Elmore, and prospered. He opened a shoe-store and secured a good run of trade.

Socially he was also a success and made many friends. And he accomplished the wish of his heart. He met Miss Annabel Adams, and became more and more captivated by her charms.

At the end of a year the situation of Mr. Ralph Spencer was this: he had won the respect of the community, his shoe-store was flour-

ishing, and he and Annabel were engaged to be married in two weeks.
Mr. Adams, the typical, plodding country banker, approved of
Spencer. Annabel's pride in him almost equaled her affection. He
was as much at home in the family of Mr. Adams and that of Annabel's married sister as if he were already a member.

One day Jimmy sat down in his room and wrote this letter, which
he mailed to the safe address of one of his old friends in St. Louis:

Dear Old Pal:

I want you to be at Sullivan's place in Little Rock, next Wednesday night, at nine o'clock. I want you to wind up some little matters
for me. And, also, I want to make you a present of my kit of tools.
I know you'll be glad to get them—you couldn't duplicate the lot
for a thousand dollars. Say, Billy, I've quit the old business—a year
ago. I've got a nice store. I'm making an honest living, and I'm going
to marry the finest girl on earth two weeks from now. It's the only
life, Billy—the straight one. I wouldn't touch a dollar of another
man's money now for a million. After I get married I'm going to sell
out and go West, where there won't be so much danger of having
old scores brought up against me. I tell you, Billy, she's an angel.
She believes in me; and I wouldn't do another crooked thing for the
whole world. Be sure to be at Sully's, for I must see you. I'll bring
along the tools with me.

> Your old friend,
> Jimmy

On the Monday night after Jimmy wrote this letter, Ben Price
jogged unobtrusively into Elmore in a livery buggy. He lounged
about town in his quiet way until he found out what he wanted to
know. From the drug-store across the street from Spencer's shoe-store,
he got a good look at Ralph D. Spencer.

"Going to marry the banker's daughter are you, Jimmy?" said Ben
to himself, softly. "Well, I don't know!"

The next morning, Jimmy took breakfast at the Adamses. He was
going to Little Rock that day to order his wedding-suit and buy
something nice for Annabel. That would be the first time he had left
town since he came to Elmore. It had been more than a year now
since those last professional "jobs," and he thought he could safely
venture out.

After breakfast quite a family party went downtown together—Mr. Adams, Annabel, Jimmy, and Annabel's married sister with her two little girls, aged five and nine. They came by the hotel where Jimmy still boarded and he ran up to his room and brought along his suitcase. Then they went on to the bank. There stood Jimmy's horse and buggy and Dolph Gibson, who was going to drive him over to the railroad station.

All went inside the high, carved oak railings into the banking room—Jimmy included, for Mr. Adams' future son-in-law was welcome anywhere. The clerks were pleased to be greeted by the good-looking, agreeable young man who was going to marry Miss Annabel. Jimmy set his suitcase down. Annabel, whose heart was bubbling with happiness and lively youth, put on Jimmy's hat, and picked up the suitcase. "Wouldn't I make a nice drummer?" said Annabel. "My, Ralph, how heavy it is! Feels like it was full of gold bricks."

"Lot of nickel-plated shoe-horns in there," said Jimmy coolly, "that I'm going to return. Thought I'd save express charges by taking them up. I'm getting awfully economical."

The Elmore Bank had just put in a new safe and vault. Mr. Adams was very proud of it, and insisted on an inspection by everyone. The vault was a small one, but it had a new, patented door. It fastened with three solid steel bolts thrown simultaneously with a single handle, and had a timelock. Mr. Adams beamingly explained its workings to Mr. Spencer, who showed a courteous but not too intelligent interest. The two children, May and Agatha, were delighted by the shining metal and funny clock and knobs.

While they were thus engaged Ben Price sauntered in and leaned on his elbow, looking casually inside between the railings. He told the teller that he didn't want anything; he was just waiting for a man he knew.

Suddenly there was a scream or two from the women, and a commotion. Unperceived by the elders, May, the nine-year-old girl, in a spirit of play, had shut Agatha in the vault. She had then shot the bolts and turned the knob of the combination as she had seen Mr. Adams do.

The old banker sprang to the handle and tugged at it for a moment. "The door can't be opened," he groaned. "The clock hasn't been wound nor the combination set."

Agatha's mother screamed again, hysterically.

"Hush!" said Mr. Adams, raising his trembling hand.

"All be quiet for a moment. Agatha," he called as loudly as he could. "Listen to me." During the following silence they could just hear the faint sound of the child wildly shrieking in the dark vault in a panic of terror.

"My precious darling!" wailed the mother. "She will die of fright! Open the door! Oh, break it open! Can't you men do something?"

"There isn't a man nearer than Little Rock who can open that door," said Mr. Adams, in a shaky voice. "My God! Spencer, what shall we do? That child—she can't stand it long in there. There isn't enough air, and, besides, she'll go into convulsions from fright."

Agatha's mother, frantic now, beat the door of the vault with her hands. Somebody wildly suggested dynamite. Annabel turned to Jimmy, her large eyes full of anguish, but not yet despairing. To a woman nothing seems quite impossible to the powers of the man she worships.

"Can't you do something, Ralph—try, won't you?"

He looked at her with a queer, soft smile on his lips and in his keen eyes.

"Annabel," he said, "give me that rose you are wearing, will you?"

Hardly believing that she heard him aright, she unpinned the bud from the bosom of her dress, and placed it in his hand. Jimmy stuffed it into his vest-pocket, threw off his coat, and pulled up his shirt-sleeves. With that act Ralph D. Spencer passed away and Jimmy Valentine took his place.

"Get away from the door, all of you," he commanded, shortly.

He set his suitcase on the table, and opened it flat. From that time on he seemed to be unconscious of the presence of anyone else. He laid out the shining, queer implements swiftly and orderly, whistling softly to himself as he always did when at work. In a deep silence and immovable, the others watched him as if under a spell.

Jimmy's pet drill was biting smoothly into the steel door. In ten minutes—breaking his own burglarious record—he threw back the bolts and opened the door.

Agatha, almost collapsed, but safe, was gathered into her mother's arms.

Jimmy Valentine put on his coat and walked outside the railings toward the front door. As he went he thought he heard a far-away voice that he once knew call "Ralph!" But he never hesitated.

At the door a big man stood somewhat in his way.

"Hello, Ben!" said Jimmy, still with his strange smile. "Got around at last, have you? Well, let's go. I don't know that it makes much difference, now."

And then Ben Price acted rather strangely.

"Guess you're mistaken, Mr. Spencer," he said. "Don't believe I recognize you. Your buggy's waiting for you, ain't it?"

And Ben Price turned and strolled down the street.

About the author

O. Henry (1862–1910) is the pen-name of William Sidney Porter, one of the most prolific of the short story writers. While he was working on newspapers in New York City, there was much talk of "The Four Hundred," the leaders of the City's social world. O. Henry chose to write about the common people, and published a collection of his stories under the title, *The Four Million*. He is the master of the surprise ending. His stories are uneven in interest and style, but the best of them carry an unforgettable single impression.

Questions for discussion

1. What does the title of this story mean? What was Jimmy's reformation? In order for something to be retrieved, or recovered, it must first be lost. In what sense, and at what point was Jimmy's reformation lost?
2. O. Henry is famous for his surprise endings. Was the ending of this story a surprise to you? How many sentences did O. Henry use to produce this surprise?
3. How much do you know about the characters? About their personalities? Their values? Their inner feelings? Is this story interesting primarily because of the characters, or because of the action?
4. Jimmy had a craftsman's pride in doing things well. Point to one word in the first sentence that shows this characteristic. Find other evidence of this characteristic in the story.
5. What is the attitude in the story toward the crime of safe-cracking? Does the author treat it lightly or seriously? Is there any evidence that Jimmy feels guilty about breaking the law?
6. FORESHADOWING. In order to be convincing, a surprise ending has to be possible in terms of the story. That is, the author has to pre-

pare the reader for the ending. He does this by planting clues along the way. This is called *foreshadowing*.

    a. How is Jimmy's interest in the shoe business foreshadowed in the first sentence?

    b. What comment of the warden foreshadows the great change in Jimmy?

    c. What act of generosity which takes place early in the story foreshadows Jimmy's final generous decision?

7. There is a change also in Ben Price. The end of the story turns upon this change. Does the author prepare you for Ben Price's decision? Is the ending reasonable?

Vocabulary growth

It is useful to have a large vocabulary, not just to impress your friends, but to understand more of what other people and books are saying. Vocabularly growth does not just happen, like measles or mumps. Vocabulary grows only through exercise—in your speech and writing and in your reading.

CONTEXT. How do you exercise your vocabulary in reading? There is one simple direction to follow: *When you come to a new word, try to figure out what it means.* Don't ignore it. Two things will help you: A knowledge of word parts and an understanding of context. The *context* of a word is the other words with which it is used.

Let's see how context works to reveal meaning. On page 17 you will find this paragraph:

> The clerk was impressed by the clothes and manner of Jimmy. He, himself, was something of a pattern of fashion to the thinly gilded youth of Elmore, but he now perceived his shortcomings. While trying to figure out Jimmy's manner of tying his four-in-hand he cordially gave information.

What does *perceived his shortcomings* mean? *Clue 1:* You can see that *his* refers to the "clerk." *Clue 2:* In *shortcomings* you recognize *short*, which means not enough. Something is missing. *Clue 3:* The clerk was impressed by Jimmy's clothes. *Clue 4:* The clerk himself was a pattern of fashion, *but now.* . . . The words *but now* are a signal that something has changed. What does *perceived* mean? You might guess: *understood, recognized, felt, saw.* Putting your guess and the clues together you might come up with this: "The clerk saw that something was missing in his own way of dressing."

Try this method with the italicized words in the following sentences from page 15:

a. The clerk handed him a railroad ticket and the five-dollar bill with which the law expected him to *rehabilitate* himself into good citizenship and prosperity.
b. Valentine, 9762, was *chronicled* on the books, "Pardoned by Governor . . ."

For composition

You will find many good examples of vivid writing in this story. The three paragraphs following "Better think over my advice, Valentine." are worth rereading for suggestions to improve your own writing. *Was* as a linking verb appears only once. Study the action words to see the way in which they make the writing more vivid.

Write one paragraph of narrative without using any form of the verb *to be*. Choose a dramatic moment in the story such as:

a. Ralph D. Spencer's fingers fumbled about in his vest-pocket and drew out a slightly battered rosebud.
b. The nine-year old May, interested in mechanical things like turning knobs on vaults, now stood before the suitcase on the table.
c. Annabel, choked with sobs, was clinging to her father.

The Necklace

GUY DE MAUPASSANT

The young bride longs for elegant gowns, sparkling jewels and gay society, but her husband's income cannot provide them. What does one do when he wants things beyond his reach? This story tells you what Monsieur and Madame Loisel did. You may judge for yourself whether the plan was a wise one.

SHE was one of those pretty and charming girls who are sometimes, as if by a mistake of destiny, born in a family of clerks. She had no dowry, no expectations, no means of being known, understood, loved, wedded, by any rich and distinguished man; and she let herself be married to a little clerk at the Ministry of Public Instruction.

She dressed plainly because she could not dress well, but she was as unhappy as though she had really fallen from her proper station; since with women there is neither caste nor rank; and beauty, grace, and charm act instead of family and birth. Natural fineness, instinct for what is elegant, suppleness of wit, are the sole hierarchy, and make from women of the people the equals of the very greatest ladies.

She suffered ceaselessly, feeling herself born for all the delicacies and all the luxuries. She suffered from the poverty of her dwelling, from the wretched look of the walls, from the worn-out chairs, from the ugliness of the curtains. All those things, of which another woman of her rank would never even have been conscious, tortured her and made her angry. The sight of the little Breton peasant who did her humble housework aroused in her regrets which were despairing, and distracted dreams. She thought of the silent ante-chambers hung with Oriental tapestry, lit by tall bronze candelabra, and of

24

the two great footmen in knee-breeches who sleep in the big arm-chairs, made drowsy by the heavy warmth of the hot-air stove. She thought of the long *salons* fitted up with ancient silk, of the delicate furniture carrying priceless curiosities, and of the coquettish per-fumed boudoirs made for talks at five o'clock with intimate friends, with men famous and sought after, whom all women envy and whose attention they all desire.

When she sat down to dinner, before the round table covered with a table-cloth three days old, opposite her husband, who un-covered the soup tureen and declared with an enchanted air, "Ah, the good *pot-au-feu!* I don't know anything better than that," she thought of dainty dinners, of shining silverware, of tapestry which peopled the walls with ancient personages and with strange birds flying in the midst of a fairy forest; and she thought of delicious dishes served on marvelous plates, and of the whispered gallantries which you listen to with a sphinx-like smile, while you are eating the pink flesh of a trout or the wings of a quail.

She had no dresses, no jewels, nothing. And she loved nothing but that; she felt made for that. She would so have liked to please, to be envied, to be charming, to be sought after.

She had a friend, a former schoolmate at the convent, who was rich, and whom she did not like to go and see any more, because she suffered so much when she came back.

But, one evening, her husband returned home with a triumphant air, and holding a large envelope in his hand.

"There," said he, "here is something for you."

She tore the paper sharply, and drew out a printed card which bore these words:

"The Minister of Public Instruction and Mme. Georges Ram-ponneau request the honor of M. and Mme. Loisel's company at the palace of the Ministry on Monday evening, January 18th."

Instead of being delighted, as her husband hoped, she threw the invitation on the table with disdain, murmuring:

"What do you want me to do with that?"

"But, my dear, I thought you would be glad. You never go out, and this is such a fine opportunity. I had awful trouble to get it. Every one wants to go; it is very select, and they are not giving many invitations to clerks. The whole official world will be there."

She looked at him with an irritated eye, and she said, impatiently:
"And what do you want me to put on my back?"

He had not thought of that; he stammered:

"Why, the dress you go to the theater in. It looks very well, to
me."

He stopped, distracted, seeing that his wife was crying. Two great
tears descended slowly from the corners of her eyes towards the
corners of her mouth. He stuttered:

"What's the matter? What's the matter?"

But, by a violent effort, she had conquered her grief, and she
replied, with a calm voice, while she wiped her wet cheeks:

"Nothing. Only I have no dress, and therefore I can't go to this
ball. Give your card to some colleague whose wife is better equipped
than I."

He was in despair. He resumed:

"Come, let us see, Mathilde. How much would it cost, a suitable
dress, which you could use on other occasions, something very
simple?"

She reflected several seconds, making her calculations and wondering also what sum she could ask without drawing on herself an immediate refusal and a frightened exclamation from the economical
clerk.

Finally, she replied, hesitatingly:

"I don't know exactly, but I think I could manage it with four
hundred francs."

He had grown a little pale, because he was laying aside just that
amount to buy a gun and treat himself to a little shooting next summer on the plain of Nanterre, with several friends who went to
shoot larks down there, of a Sunday.

But he said:

"All right. I will give you four hundred francs. And try to have
a pretty dress."

The day of the ball drew near, and Mme. Loisel seemed sad,
uneasy, anxious. Her dress was ready, however. Her husband said to
her one evening:

"What is the matter? Come, you've been so queer these last three
days."

And she answered:

"It annoys me not to have a single jewel, not a single stone, nothing to put on. I shall look like distress. I should almost rather not go at all."

He resumed:

"You might wear natural flowers. It's very stylish at this time of the year. For ten francs you can get two or three magnificent roses."

She was not convinced.

"No; there's nothing more humiliating than to look poor among other women who are rich."

But her husband cried:

"How stupid you are! Go look up your friend Mme. Forestier, and ask her to lend you some jewels. You're quite thick enough with her to do that."

She uttered a cry of joy:

"It's true. I never thought of it."

The next day she went to her friend and told of her distress.

Mme. Forestier went to a wardrobe with a glass door, took out a large jewel-box, brought it back, opened it, and said to Mme. Loisel:

"Choose, my dear."

She saw first of all some bracelets, then a pearl necklace, then a Venetian cross, gold, and precious stones of admirable workmanship. She tried on the ornaments before the glass, hesitated, could not make up her mind to part with them, to give them back. She kept asking:

"Haven't you any more?"

"Why, yes. Look. I don't know what you like."

All of a sudden she discovered, in a black satin box, a superb necklace of diamonds; and her heart began to beat with an immoderate desire. Her hands trembled as she took it. She fastened it around her throat, outside her high-necked dress, and remained lost in ecstasy at the sight of herself.

Then she asked, hesitatingly, filled with anguish:

"Can you lend me that, only that?"

"Why, yes, certainly."

She sprang upon the neck of her friend, kissed her passionately, then fled with her treasure.

The day of the ball arrived. Mme. Loisel made a great success. She was prettier than them all, elegant, gracious, smiling, and crazy with joy. All the men looked at her, asked her name, endeavored to be introduced. All the attachés of the Cabinet wanted to waltz with her. She was remarked by the minister himself.

She danced with intoxication, with passion, made drunk by pleasure, forgetting all, in the triumph of her beauty, in the glory of her success, in a sort of cloud of happiness composed of all this homage, of all this admiration, of all these awakened desires, and of that sense of complete victory which is so sweet to woman's heart.

She went away about four o'clock in the morning. Her husband had been sleeping since midnight, in a little deserted anteroom, with three other gentlemen whose wives were having a good time.

He threw over her shoulders the wraps which he had brought, modest wraps of common life, whose poverty contrasted with the elegance of the ball dress. She felt this and wanted to escape so as not to be remarked by the other women, who were enveloping themselves in costly furs.

Loisel held her back.

"Wait a bit. You will catch cold outside. I will go and call a cab."

But she did not listen to him, and rapidly descended the stairs. When they were in the street they did not find a carriage; and they began to look for one, shouting after the cabmen whom they saw passing by at a distance.

They went down towards the Seine, in despair, shivering with cold. At last they found on the quay one of those ancient noctambulant coupés which, exactly as if they were ashamed to show their misery during the day, are never seen around Paris until after nightfall.

It took them to their door in the Rue des Martyrs, and once more, sadly, they climbed up homeward. All was ended for her. And as to him, he reflected that he must be at the Ministry at ten o'clock.

She removed the wraps, which covered her shoulders, before the glass, so as once more to see herself in all her glory. But suddenly she uttered a cry. She had no longer the necklace around her neck!

Her husband already half-undressed, demanded:

"What is the matter with you?"

She turned madly towards him:

"I have—I have—I've lost Mme. Forestier's necklace."

He stood up, distracted.

"What!—how?—Impossible!"

And they looked in the folds of her dress, in the folds of her cloak, in her pockets, everywhere. They did not find it.

He asked:

"You're sure you had it on when you left the ball?"

"Yes, I felt it in the vestibule of the palace."

"But if you had lost it in the street we should have heard it fall. It must be in the cab."

"Yes. Probably. Did you take his number?"

"No. And you, didn't you notice it?"

"No."

They looked, thunderstruck, at one another. At last Loisel put on his clothes.

"I shall go back on foot," said he, "over the whole route which we have taken, to see if I can't find it."

And he went out. She sat waiting on a chair in her ball dress, without strength to go to bed, overwhelmed, without fire, without a thought.

Her husband came back about seven o'clock. He had found nothing.

He went to Police Headquarters, to the newspaper offices, to offer a reward; he went to the cab companies—everywhere, in fact, whither he was urged by the least suspicion of hope.

She waited all day, in the same condition of mad fear before this terrible calamity.

Loisel returned at night with a hollow, pale face; he had discovered nothing.

"You must write to your friend," said he, "that you have broken the clasp of her necklace and that you are having it mended. That will give us time to turn round."

She wrote at his dictation.

At the end of the week they had lost all hope.

And Loisel, who had aged five years, declared:

"We must consider how to replace that ornament."

The next day they took the box which had contained it, and they went to the jeweler whose name was found within. He consulted his books.

"It was not I, madame, who sold that necklace; I must simply have furnished the case."

Then they went from jeweler to jeweler, searching for a necklace like the other, consulting their memories, sick both of them with chagrin and with anguish.

They found, in a shop at the Palais Royal, a string of diamonds which seemed to them exactly like the one they looked for. It was worth forty thousand francs. They could have it for thirty-six.

So they begged the jeweler not to sell it for three days yet. And they made a bargain that he should buy it back for thirty-four thousand francs, in case they found the other one before the end of February.

Loisel possessed eighteen thousand francs which his father had left him. He would borrow the rest.

He did borrow, asking a thousand francs of one, five hundred of another, five louis here, three louis there. He gave notes, took up ruinous obligations, dealt with usurers, and all the race of lenders. He compromised all the rest of his life, risked his signature without even knowing if he could meet it; and, frightened by the pains yet to come, by the black misery which was about to fall upon him, by the prospect of all the physical privations and of all the moral tortures which he was to suffer, he went to get the new necklace, putting down upon the merchant's counter thirty-six thousand francs.

When Mme. Loisel took back the necklace Mme. Forestier said to her, with a chilly manner:

"You should have returned it sooner, I might have needed it."

She did not open the case, as her friend had so much feared. If she had detected the substitution, what would she have thought, what would she have said? Would she not have taken Mme. Loisel for a thief?

Mme. Loisel now knew the horrible existence of the needy. She took her part, moreover, all on a sudden, with heroism. That dreadful debt must be paid. She would pay it. They dismissed their servant; they changed their lodgings; they rented a garret under the roof.

She came to know what heavy housework meant and the odious cares of the kitchen. She washed the dishes, using her rosy nails on the pots and pans. She washed the dirty linen, the shirts, and the dish-cloths, which she dried upon a line; she carried the slops down to the street every morning, and carried up the water, stopping for breath at every landing. And, dressed like a woman of the people, she went to the fruiterer, the grocer, the butcher, her basket on her arm, bargaining, insulted, defending her miserable money sou by sou.

Each month they had to meet some notes, renew others, obtain more time.

Her husband worked in the evening making a fair copy of some tradesman's accounts, and late at night he often copied manuscript for five sous a page.

And this life lasted ten years.

At the end of ten years they had paid everything, everything with the rates of usury, and the accumulations of the compound interest.

Mme. Loisel looked old now. She had become the woman of impoverished households—strong and hard and rough. With frowsy hair, skirts askew, and red hands, she talked loud while washing the floor with great swishes of water. But sometimes, when her husband was at the office, she sat down near the window, and she thought of that gay evening of long ago, of that ball where she had been so beautiful and so fêted.

What would have happened if she had not lost that necklace? Who knows? Who knows? How life is strange and how changeful! How little a thing is needed for us to be lost or to be saved!

But, one Sunday, having gone to take a walk in the Champs Elysées to refresh herself from the labors of the week, she suddenly perceived a woman who was leading a child. It was Mme. Forestier, still young, still beautiful, still charming.

Mme. Loisel felt moved. Was she going to speak to her? Yes, certainly. And now that she had paid, she was going to tell her all about it. Why not?

She went up.

"Good-day, Jeanne."

The other, astonished to be familiarly addressed by this plain good-wife, did not recognize her at all, and stammered:

"But—madame!—I do not know—You must be mistaken."

"No. I am Mathilde Loisel."

Her friend uttered a cry.

"Oh, my poor Mathilde! How you are changed!"

"Yes, I have had days hard enough, since I have seen you, days wretched enough—and that because of you!"

"Of me! How so?"

"Do you remember that diamond necklace which you lent me to wear at the ministerial ball?"

"Yes. Well?"

"Well, I lost it."

"What do you mean? You brought it back."

"I brought you back another just like it. And for this we have been ten years paying. You can understand that it was not easy for us, us who had nothing. At last it is ended, and I am very glad."

Mme. Forestier had stopped.

"You say that you bought a necklace of diamonds to replace mine?"

"Yes. You never noticed it, then! They were very like."

And she smiled with a joy which was proud and naïve at once.

Mme. Forestier, strongly moved, took her two hands.

"Oh, my poor Mathilde! Why, my necklace was paste.[1] It was worth at most five hundred francs!"

About the author

Guy de Maupassant (1850–1893) is the most famous of French short story writers. Indeed, he is one of the greatest short story writers of all time. He has an objective way of presenting characters and situations as though he himself were not involved with them. *The Necklace* is generally regarded as one of the best short stories in world literature. De Maupassant wrote several novels, a play, and a volume of poetry in addition to short stories.

Questions for discussion

1. Did the Loisel's deserve their fate? Did they suffer because of weaknesses in their characters, and because of their mistakes? Before you answer this question, go to the next four questions.
2. What is Madame Loisel's chief interest in life when you first meet her? Does she ever lose this interest? What trait do you see when she first visits Madame Forestier?
3. What evidence is there that in her early years Madame Loisel was the sort of person who could have had a career in society?
4. Was Monsieur Loisel a good husband? Explain your answer. Madame Loisel had one evening of glory as a joyful memory. Did her husband have a comparable satisfaction? Did the hardships they both suffered seem to be equally divided? If not, who seemed to carry the greater burden?

[1] **paste:** a hard, brilliant glass used to make artificial gems

5. Did the Loisels act sensibly in their efforts to restore the necklace? What else might they have done? They took the hard way out of their situation. What does this show about their characters? Now go back and consider the first question.

6. Were you surprised at the ending? Does it seem reasonable? The author has prepared you for this by giving an important clue. You will find the clue on page 29.

7. Some writers use *irony* to build up the power and total effect of their stories. Irony may be defined as a combination of circumstances that is the opposite of what is appropriate or expected. Thus, it would be ironical if a fire engine were destroyed by fire, or if a safety patrol car were demolished in an accident.

   At the close of the story, it is clear that Madame Forestier owes the Loisels many thousands of francs. Supposing that the money was repaid, what irony would there be in the fact that Madame Loisel could then afford pretty dresses and other extravagances?

   Do you see anything ironical in the fact that Monsieur Loisel worked so hard to get a ticket to the ball, and was so pleased at his success?

8. Did the ending of the story seem to you sad or happy? If this story were to be made into a motion picture, would the ending have to be changed? Do stories always have to end happily?

Vocabulary growth

CONTEXT. You cannot expect to get the complete meaning of a word from one experience with it. You can often grasp the meaning of a word by examining the words that come just before, and directly after that word in the sentence. These words are the *context*, and the meaning of a word depends upon the context in which it appears. Context clues will often give you enough of an idea of the meaning of unfamiliar words to enable you to continue with your reading. By examining their contexts, what meaning do you get from the following italicized words:

a. They had paid everything with the *rates* of *usury*, and the *accumulation* of *compound interest*.

b. He *compromised* all the rest of his life.

c. ". . . a cloud of happiness *composed* of all this *homage*, of all this admiration . . ."

For composition

1. How far should one go to perform his duty? Is it ever one's duty to give up one's life? Is it ever one's duty to give up all chances of being

married? Circumstances determine the answers, do they not? To protect his country, a soldier may have to give up his life. How does anyone decide what he must do out of duty? To what and to whom does the average person have duties? Write a paper on your views about duty. Describe what you feel to be your duties, and what you would do in order to carry them out.

2. Would you like to try to write a short story? Write the sequel to "The Necklace." What happens to the Loisels? What conflicts might arise? How would they be settled? What surprise endings can you imagine? If you use a surprise ending, make sure that you prepare your readers for it.

The Lost Brooch

ANTON CHEKHOV

An article of value is lost. The finger of suspicion points from one person to another. People react to suspicion in surprising ways as you will discover.

In many Russian stories the same character may have several names. A daughter of a man whose name is Peter may be called Petrovna (meaning daughter of Peter), but she may have, in addition, first names which have been given her at birth or when she was christened. If she is married, her husband's last name also becomes a part of her name. The same person may also have nicknames which you will not recognize as quickly as you would recognize the nickname Jim for James. In this story Theodosia Vasilevny, Madame Kushkina, and Fenya are all names for the same person. Nicolai Sergeitch is her husband. Kushkin is his last name, but his wife is called Madame Kushkina, the *a* is added to indicate the feminine form of her husband's last name.

Mashenka Pavletsky, a young girl who had just finished her studies at boarding school, returning home from a walk, to the house of the Kushkins, where she was living as a governess, came upon an extraordinary commotion. The doorman, Michael, who let her in, was agitated and red as a lobster. A commotion could be heard from upstairs.

"The mistress is probably having one of her spells," Mashenka thought, "or she has been quarreling with her husband."

In the reception room and in the hall she ran into some of the maids. One servant was crying. Then Mashenka saw the master himself run out of her room. This Nicolai Sergeitch, though not yet old, had a flabby face and a big bald spot. He was red in the face. He shuddered. Taking no notice of the governess, he went past her and throwing up his hands, exclaimed, "Oh, how ghastly this is! How tactless! How stupid, absurd! It's abominable!"

Mashenka stepped into her room and there, for the first time in her life, she experienced in all of its acuteness the feeling which is so familiar to all timid people in a subordinate position, living on the bread of the rich and powerful. They were making a search of her room. The mistress, Theodosia Vasilevny, a plump, broad-shouldered woman with heavy black eyebrows under her cap, uncouth, with a slight growth of mustache, with red hands and face, and in her manners resembling a rude country cook, was standing at her table and putting back into her workbag balls of wool, scraps, and slips of paper. Evidently the appearance of the governess took her by surprise, as, looking up and catching sight of her white, astonished face, she became somewhat embarrassed and stammered, "Pardon, I . . . accidentally spilled . . . I caught my sleeve . . ."

And still mumbling something, Madame Kushkina gave a swish to her train and went out. Mashenka looked around her room with amazement, and understanding nothing, not knowing what to think, shrugged her shoulders and turned cold with fear. What was Theodosia Vasilevny looking for in her bag? If, as she said, she had really caught her sleeve in it and spilled it, then why had Nicolai Sergeitch dashed out of her room looking so red and excited? Why was one of the table drawers partly open? The money box, in which the governess kept coins and old stamps locked up, was unfastened. They had opened it, but they had not been able to lock it, although they had covered the whole lock with scratches. The bookstand, the top of the table, the bed—all bore fresh traces of the search. And the basket with the linen, too. The linen was neatly folded, but not in that order in which Mashenka had left it on going out of the house. This meant that it was really a search, but what was the object of it? What had happened? Mashenka recalled the agitation of the doorman, the commotion, which was still going on, the crying servant; didn't all this have some connection with the search that had just taken place in her room? Wasn't she involved in some terrible affair? Mashenka turned pale, and, cold all over, she sank down on the linen basket.

A servant came into the room.

"Liza, don't you know that they . . . have been searching in my room?" asked the governess.

"A brooch of the mistress worth two thousand rubles has been lost."

"Yes, but why search me?"

"They searched everybody, Miss. They went through everything of mine, too. They stripped us all stark naked and searched us. And there I was, Miss, as before God. I never even went near her toilet table, let alone touching the brooch. And I shall tell that to the police, too."

"But . . . why search me?" continued the governess, unable to understand.

"Someone stole the brooch, I tell you. . . . The mistress herself searched everybody with her own hands. They even searched Michael, the doorman, himself. A downright scandal! Nicolai Sergeitch just looks on, cackling like a hen. But there's no need for you to be upset about this, Miss. They didn't find anything in your room! As long as you didn't take the brooch there's nothing for you to be afraid of."

"But this is vile, Liza . . . insulting," said Mashenka, choking with indignation. "This is baseness, meanness! What right had she to suspect me and to ransack my things?"

"You are living amongst strangers, Miss," sighed Liza. "Although you are a young lady, yet . . . it's as if you were a servant. . . . This isn't like being at home with papa and mama."

Mashenka threw herself down on the bed and began to sob bitterly. Never before had such an outrage been perpetrated against her, never had she been so deeply insulted as now. . . . They had suspected her, a well-bred, sensitive girl, the daughter of a professor, of stealing; they had searched her like a woman of the streets! It would be impossible, seemingly, to conceive of any insult greater than that. And to this feeling of outrage was added another heavy fear: what might happen now? All sorts of absurd ideas came into her mind. If they were capable of suspecting her of stealing, then that meant that they might arrest her, strip her stark naked and search her, and then lead her through the street under guard, imprison her in a dark, cold cell with mice and vermin, in just the sort of place they put Princess Tarakanova. Who would intercede for her? Her people lived far away in the provinces; they hadn't the money to come to her. She was alone in the great city as in a great field, without relatives, without acquaintances. They could do with her what they wished.

"I shall run to all the judges and lawyers," thought Mashenka shuddering. "I shall explain to them, I shall take oath. . . . They will prove that I cannot be the thief."

Mashenka recalled that in her room in the basket, under the sheets, were lying some sweets, that, following an old habit established at boarding school, she had put into her pocket at dinner and had carried off to her room with her. The thought that this little secret of hers was already known to her master and mistress threw her into a fever, and the result of all this, the fear, the shame, the insult, was that her heart began to palpitate violently and made itself felt in her temples, her hands, and deep within her.

"Dinner is served!" They were calling Mashenka. Should she go down or not? Mashenka smoothed her hair, wiped her face with a wet towel, and went into the dining room. There dinner was already begun. At one end of the table sat Theodosia Vasilevny, pompous, with a grave, stupid face; at the other end was Nicolai Sergeitch. At the sides sat the guests and the children. Two footmen in frock coats and white gloves served the dinner. Everybody knew that there had been a commotion in the house, that the mistress was upset, and all kept silent. Nothing was heard but their chewing and the clatter of the spoons against the plates.

The mistress herself opened the conversation.

"What have we for the third course?" she asked the footman in a dull, martyred voice.

"Sturgeon *a la russe*," answered the footman.

"I ordered that, Fenya," Nicolai Sergeitch made haste to say. "I was hungry for fish. If you don't like it, my dear, then don't have them serve it. You see I . . . among the rest . . ."

Theodosia Vasilevny did not like dishes that she had not ordered herself, and now her eyes filled with tears.

"There, there, let's not get upset," said Mamikov, her family doctor, in a sirupy voice as he lightly patted her hand and smiled sweetly. "We are nervous enough without that. Let's forget about the brooch. One's health is more precious than two thousand rubles."

"I don't care about the miserable two thousand!" answered the mistress, and a big tear ran down her cheek. "The fact itself fills me with indignation! I have never put up with stealing in my house. I am not sorry, I am not sorry about anything. But to steal in my house—that is such ungratefulness! To repay me in such a way for my kindness!"

Everyone looked at his plate, but it seemed to Mashenka that after what the mistress said everyone was staring at her. Suddenly a lump came into her throat; she began to cry and pressed her handkerchief to her face.

"Pardon . . ." she stammered, "I cannot. My head aches. I am going."

And she rose from the table, awkwardly banging her chair and more disconcerted than ever went out.

"God knows," said Nicolai Sergeitch, "there was no need to make a search in her room. How ridiculous that was, really!"

"I do not say that she took the brooch," said Theodosia Vasilevny, "but you can vouch for her, I suppose? I confess, I put little trust in these learned paupers."

"Really, Fenya, it is beside the point. Excuse me, Fenya, but according to law you haven't the right to search anyone."

"I don't know anything about your laws. I only know that my brooch is gone, that is all. And I'm going to find that brooch," and she hit her fork against her plate, her eyes flashing with anger. "And you go ahead and eat and don't interfere with my affairs."

Nicolai Sergeitch meekly dropped his eyes and sighed. Meanwhile, Mashenka, having reached her room, threw herself on the bed. She was no longer frightened or ashamed, but a violent desire obsessed her to slap the face of this hard, this arrogant, stupid, smug woman.

As she lay there, breathing hard into the pillow, she dreamed how sweet it would be to go right now and buy the most costly brooch and fling it into the face of this stupid and unreasonable woman. If God would only let Theodosia Vasilevny be brought to ruin, so that she would have to go begging and might understand all the horror of poverty and of not being one's own master, and if the outraged Mashenka might only offer her charity. Oh, if she might only fall heir to a large fortune, buy a carriage, and ride dashingly past her windows that she might envy her.

But all this was daydreaming; in reality there was only one thing to do, to go away as quickly as possible, not to remain here even a single hour. True, it was terrible to give up her place, to go back to her people who had nothing, but what could she do? Mashenka couldn't look at her mistress again, nor at her little room; she was stifled here, full of horror. Theodosia Vasilevny, daft on the subject of diseases and of her would-be aristocracy, was so repulsive to her that it seemed as if everything in the world became gross and ugly because of the fact that this woman was in existence. Mashenka jumped up from the bed and began to pack.

"May I come in?" asked Nicolai Sergeitch at the door; he had come to the door noiselessly and spoke in a soft, gentle voice. "May I?"

"Come in." He came in and remained standing at the door. His eyes looked dim and his little red nose shone. He had been drinking beer after dinner, and this was evidenced in his gait and in his weak flabby hands.

"What does this mean?" he asked pointing to the basket.

"I am packing. I am sorry, Nicolai Sergeitch, but I can't stay in your house any longer. This search has offended me deeply!"

"I understand. Only there's no need of doing this. Why? Your room was searched, but you . . . what difference does that make to you? You will lose nothing because of that."

Mashenka was silent and went on packing. Nicolai Sergeitch kept worrying his mustache as if trying to think what else to say and continued in a wheedling voice:

"I understand, of course, but you must be forbearing. You know my wife is excitable, flighty; you mustn't judge her harshly."

Mashenka said nothing.

"If you are so offended," continued Nicolai Sergeitch, "well, then . . . I am ready to apologize before you. I am sorry."

Mashenka made no answer but only bent lower over her trunk. This hollow-cheeked, spineless creature was of no significance whatever in the house. He played the miserable part of a weakling and somebody always in the way even for the servants; and his apology, likewise, meant nothing.

"M-m- . . . you say nothing? This isn't enough for you? In that case I apologize for my wife. In the name of my wife. . . . She didn't behave with much tact, I admit like a gentleman."

Nicolai Sergeitch walked about, sighed, and went on: "That means you want to keep on gnawing me here, beneath my heart. . . . You want my conscience to torment me."

"I know, Nicolai Sergeitch, you are not to blame," said Mashenka, looking straight into his face with her big, tear-stained eyes. "Why then do you fret yourself?"

"Of course, but for all that . . . don't go away . . . I beg you."

Mashenka shook her head in sign of negation. Nicolai Sergeitch remained standing at the window and began drumming on the window with his finger tips.

"For me such misunderstandings are simply torture," he said. "How about my getting down on my knees before you, eh, how would that be? Your pride has been offended, and here you are crying and getting ready to go away; but here I am with some pride, too, and you have no mercy on it. Or do you want me to tell you what I shall not tell even in confession? Listen, you want me to confess to what I shall not confess to a soul even in the face of death?"

Mashenka did not answer.

"I took my wife's brooch!" said Nicolai Sergeitch quickly. "Are you satisfied now? Does that make it all right? Yes, I . . . took it. . . . Only, of course, I count on your discretion. For God's sake, not a word to anyone, not half a hint!"

Mashenka, amazed and startled, went on packing; she caught up her things, crumpled them, and without any kind of order stuffed them into the trunk and the basket. Now, after the outspoken confession made by Nicolai Sergeitch, she could not remain a minute longer, and she no longer understood how she had been able to live in this house before.

"And it's no wonder . . ." continued Nicolai Sergeitch after a long silence. "The usual story. I need money, and she doesn't give me any. This house and all these things belonged to my father. All this is mine, and the brooch belonged to my mother, and . . . everything is mine. But she has seized everything, taken possession of everything. . . . I can't go to court with her . . . you agree. I beg you earnestly, forgive me . . . and stay. *Tout comprendre, tout pardonner.*[1] Will you stay?"

"No," said Mashenka with decision, beginning to tremble. "Let me alone, I beg you."

"Well, God be with you," sighed Nicolai Sergeitch, sitting down on a stool near the trunk.

"I confess, I like those people who can still be offended, who can feel scorn, and so on. I could sit here a hundred years and look at your indignant face. . . . So then, you won't stay? I understand. . . . It has to be so . . . yes, of course. It is easy for you, but for me—tsk, tsk. . . . And not a step out of this cellar. I might go to

---

[1] **Tout comprendre, tout pardonner:** To understand all is to pardon all.

one of our estates, but there are these scoundrels of my wife every-where . . . agronomists, stewards, devil take them. They mortgage and remortgage. . . . You mustn't catch the fish, keep off the grass —don't break the trees."

"Nicolai Sergeitch!" Theodosia Vasilevny's voice was heard from the drawing room. "Agnia, call the master."

"So you won't stay?" asked Nicolai Sergeitch, rising hastily and moving toward the door. "You might just as well stay. In the evenings I could drop in to see you . . . we could talk, eh? Will you stay? If you go, in the whole house there won't be one human face. Oh, this is awful!"

The pallid, hollow-cheeked face of Nicolai Sergeitch implored her, but Mashenka shook her head, and with a wave of the hand he went out.

In half an hour she was already on her way.

About the author

Anton Chekhov (1860–1904) was born in South Russia, the son of a freed serf. Though he was educated at the University of Moscow to be a physician, he never practiced his profession. He turned instead to writing, and won for himself the reputation of being Russia's foremost writer of short stories. Aside from his great achievement as a writer of short stories, he was also a master dramatist, having written such memorable stage works as *Uncle Vanya*, *The Cherry Orchard*, and *Three Sisters*. In 1961 there was a revival of three of his one-act plays in an off-Broadway production in New York.

Questions for discussion

1. Was Mashenka actually accused of stealing the brooch? Was she singled out as being more suspicious than any of the others? Why was she so outraged by the search? Why did she decide to leave?
2. Did Mashenka do the right thing by leaving? What else might she have done.
3. What Mashenka did is contrasted with what she would have liked to do, as expressed in her daydream. Which was the wiser and more mature reaction—the daydream or the abrupt departure?
4. Did the ending of the story satisfy you? Why, or why not? Would it have been a better story if Mashenka had confronted Madame Kush-

kina and criticized her actions? What details in the story make such an action impossible?

5. Why didn't Mashenka go directly to Madame Kushkina's and reveal at once the name of the real thief? What would she have gained by doing this?

6. What kind of things seem important to Madame Kushkina? Does her husband share these interests?

7. FORESHADOWING. There are several instances of planted clues, or foreshadowing which explain Nicolai Sergeitch's surprising actions. At our first sight of him, he rushes past Mashenka without speaking. Why? What has upset him? As the dinner begins, Nicolai apologizes for ordering the fish. How does this foreshadow the revelation he makes to Mashenka? What is Nicolai's reaction to his wife's search for the brooch? What does this point to later in the story?

8. Do you feel sorry for Nicolai Sergeitch, or do you feel that he deserves little sympathy? Explain.

9. Why does Nicolai confess to Mashenka? Why does he want her to stay? Docs his confession to her make him the gentleman that he claims to be?

Vocabulary growth

FIGURES OF SPEECH. A figure of speech is a literary device used to arouse a vivid picture in the imagination of the reader. The *simile* and the *metaphor* are very frequently used. Both indicate comparisons. The simile uses *as* or *like* to state the comparison. The vivid effect arises out of the fact that the two things compared are really unlike except in the one respect used in the comparison. "Michael—was agitated and *red as a lobster*." "Nicolai Sergeitch—*cackling like a hen*—" "She was alone in the city *as in a great field*." These are similes. The metaphor states a comparison or likeness without making use of the word *like* or *as*. "—you want to keep on *gnawing* me here, beneath my heart . . . You want my conscience to torment me." Was Mashenka really gnawing Nicolai Sergeitch? A rat or some such horrible creature gnaws, but here, the author compares this sort of animal behavior to a human's actions. Make a list of all similes and metaphors that you can find in this story.

For composition

Anton Chekhov died in Russia in 1904, approximately fifty years after the death of Edgar Allan Poe in the United States. Chekhov was not greatly concerned with the strong single emotional effect which Poe emphasized. Nor did he work out plots as dramatic as those of Guy de Maupassant who was writing in France at the same time that Chekhov was writing. The Russian writer focused his attention upon character. His stories are simply and realistically told. His characters are like the people he observed in real life around him. "The Lost Brooch" has several fine studies of characters. The following suggestions may help you to gain a better understanding of these characters.

1. Reread Mashenka's daydream on page 39. Write a daydream for Nicolai Sergeitch which comes to him when he first realizes that Mashenka has gone and that he is now all alone with his arrogant wife.

2. Imagine that Mashenka kept a diary. Write the entry that she made on the evening of that terrible day.

3. The story is written from an omniscient (all-knowing) point of view with the author inside and outside the minds of the characters. How would the story sound if written in the first person? Try writing an account of Mashenka's arrival home at the opening of the story. Write it in the first person from Nicolai's point of view. You might begin, "I could stand it no longer. My wife was impossible, insulting everyone, searching everything. I rushed out of Mashenka's room—."

The Tiger's Heart

JIM KJELGAARD

To do the impossible was not enough. To remain master of his village, Pepe Garcia had to do the impossible in his own way. You are about to enter village life in the exotic jungles of Latin America.

THE approaching jungle night was, in itself, a threat. As it deepened, an eerie silence enveloped the thatched village. People were silent. Tethered cattle stood quietly. Roosting chickens did not stir and wise goats made no noise. Thus it had been for countless centuries and thus it would continue to be. The brown-skinned inhabitants of the village knew the jungle. They had trodden its dim paths, forded its sulky rivers, borne its streaming heat and were intimately acquainted with its deer, tapir, crocodiles, screaming green parrots and countless other creatures.

That was the daytime jungle they could see, feel and hear, but at night everything became different. When darkness came, the jungle was alive with strange and horrible things which no man had ever seen and no man could describe. They were shadows that had no substance and one was unaware of them until they struck and killed. Then, with morning, they changed themselves back into the shape of familiar things. Because it was a time of the unknown, night had to be a time of fear.

Except, Pepe Garcia reflected, to the man who owned a rifle. As the night closed in, Pepe reached out to fondle his rifle and make sure that it was close beside him. As long as it was, he was king.

That was only just, for the rifle had cost him dearly. With eleven others from his village, Pepe had gone to help chop a right of way for the new road. They used machetes, the indispensable long knife of all jungle dwellers, and they had worked hard. Unlike the rest, Pepe had saved every peso he didn't have to spend for immediate

45

living expenses. With his savings, and after some haggling, he had bought his muzzle-loading rifle, a supply of powder, lead, and a mold in which he could fashion bullets for his rifle.

Eighty pesos the rifle had cost him. But it was worth the price. Though the jungle at night was fear itself, no man with a rifle had to fear. The others, who had only machetes with which to guard themselves from the terrors that came in the darkness, were willing to pay well for protection. Pepe went peacefully to sleep.

He did not know what awakened him, only that something was about. He listened intently, but there was no change in the jungle's monotonous night sounds. Still, something was not as it should be.

Then he heard it. At the far end of the village, near Juan Aria's hut, a goat bleated uneasily. Silence followed. The goat bleated again, louder and more fearful. There was a pattering rush of small hoofs, a frightened bleat cut short, again silence.

Pepe, who did not need to people the night with fantastic creatures because he owned a rifle, interpreted correctly what he had heard. A tiger, a jaguar, had come in the night, leaped the thorn fence with which the village was surrounded, and made off with one of Juan Aria's goats.

Pepe went peacefully back to sleep. With morning, certainly, Juan Aria would come to him.

He did not awaken until the sun was up. Then he emerged from his hut, breakfasted on a papaya he had gathered the day before, and awaited his expected visitor. They must always come to him; it ill befitted a man with a rifle to seek out anyone at all.

Presently Pepe saw two men, Juan Aria and his brother, coming up one of the paths that wound through the village. Others stared curiously, but nobody else came because their flocks had not been raided. They had no wish to pay, or to help pay, a hunter.

Pepe waited until the two were near, then said, "Buenos dias."

"Buenos dias," they replied.

They sat down in the sun, looking at nothing in particular, not afraid any more, because the day was never a time of fear. By daylight, only now and again did a tiger come to raid a flock of goats, or kill a burro or a cow.

After a suitable lapse of time, Juan Aria said, "I brought my goats into the village last night, thinking they would be safe."

"And were they not?"

"They were not. Something came and killed one, a fine white and black nanny, my favorite. When the thing left, the goat went too. Never again shall I see her alive."

"What killed your goat?" Pepe inquired.

"A devil, but this morning I saw only the tracks of a tiger."

"Did you hear it come?"

"I heard it."

"Then why did you not defend your flock?"

Juan Aria gestured with eloquent hands. "To attack a devil, or a tiger, with nothing but a machete would be madness."

"That is true," Pepe agreed. "Let us hope that the next time it is hungry, this devil, or tiger, will not come back for another goat."

"But it will!"

Pepe relaxed, for Juan Aria's admission greatly improved Pepe's bargaining position. And it was true that, having had a taste of easy game, the tiger would come again. Only death would end his forays, and since he knew where to find Juan Aria's goats, he would continue to attack them.

Pepe said, "That is bad, for a man may lose many goats to a tiger."

"Unless a hunter kills him," Juan Aria said.

"Unless a hunter kills him," Pepe agreed.

"That is why I have come to you, Pepe," Juan Aria said. A troubled frown overspread his face. "I hope you will follow and kill this tiger, for you are the only man who can do so."

"It would give me pleasure to kill him, but I cannot work for nothing."

"Nor do I expect you to. Even a tiger will not eat an entire goat, and you are sure to find what is left of my favorite nanny. Whatever the tiger has not eaten, you may have for your pay."

Pepe bristled. "You are saying that I should put myself and my rifle to work for carrion left by a tiger?"

"No, no!" Juan Aria protested. "In addition I will give you one live goat!"

"Three goats."

"I am a poor man!" the other wailed. "You would bankrupt me!"

"No man with twenty-nine goats is poor, though he may be if a tiger raids his flock a sufficient number of times," Pepe said.

"I will give you one goat and two kids."

"Two goats and one kid."

"You drive a hard bargain," Juan Aria said, "but I cannot deny you now. Kill the tiger."

Affecting an air of nonchalance, as befitted the owner of a firearm, Pepe took his rifle from the fine blanket upon which it lay when he was not carrying it. He looked to his powder horn and bullet pouch, strapped his machete on, and sauntered toward Juan Aria's hut. A half-dozen worshipful children followed.

"Begone!" Pepe ordered.

They fell behind, but continued to follow until Pepe came to that place where Juan Aria's flock had passed the night. He glanced at the dust, and saw the tiger's great paw marks imprinted there. It was a huge cat, lame in the right front paw, or it might have been injured in battle with another tiger.

Expertly, Pepe located the place where it had gone back over the thorn fence. Though the tiger had carried the sixty-pound goat in its jaws, only a couple of thorns were disturbed at the place where it had leaped.

Though he did not look around, Pepe was aware of the villagers watching him and he knew that their glances would be very respectful. Most of the men went into the jungle from time to time to work with their machetes, but none would work where tigers were known to be. Not one would dare take a tiger's trail. Only Pepe dared and, because he did, he must be revered.

Still affecting nonchalance, Pepe sauntered through the gate. Behind him, he heard the village's collective sigh of mingled relief and admiration. A raiding tiger was a very real and terrible threat, and goats and cattle were not easily come by. The man with a rifle, the man able to protect them, must necessarily be a hero.

Once in the jungle, and out of the villagers' sight, Pepe underwent a transformation.

He shed his air of indifference and became as alert as the little doe that showed him only her white tail. A rifle might be a symbol of power, but unless a man was also a hunter, a rifle did him no good. Impressing the villagers was one thing: hunting a tiger was quite another.

Pepe knew the great cats were dappled death incarnate. They could move with incredible swiftness and were strong enough to kill an ox. They feared nothing.

Jungle-born, Pepe slipped along as softly as a jungle shadow. His machete slipped a little, and he shifted it to a place where his legs would not be bumped. From time to time he glanced at the ground before him.

To trained eyes, there was a distinct trail. It consisted of an occasional drop of blood from the dead goat, a bent or broken plant, a few hairs where the tiger had squeezed between trees, paw prints in soft places. Within the first quarter mile Pepe knew many things about this tiger.

He was not an ordinary beast, or he would have gone only far enough from the village so his nostrils could not be assailed by its unwelcome scents and eaten what he wanted there, then covered the remainder of the goat with sticks and leaves. He was not old, for his was not the lagging gait of an old cat, and the ease with which he had leaped the thorn fence with a goat in his jaws was evidence of his strength.

Pepe stopped to look to the loading and priming of his rifle. There seemed to be nothing amiss, and there had better not be. When he saw the tiger, he must shoot straight and true. Warned by some super jungle sense, Pepe slowed his pace. A moment later he found his game.

He came upon it suddenly in a grove of scattered palms. Because he had not expected it there, Pepe did not see it until it was nearer than safety allowed.

The tiger crouched at the base of a palm whose fronds waved at least fifty feet above the roots. Both the beast's front paws were on what remained of the dead goat. It did not snarl or grimace, or even twitch its tail. But there was a lethal quality about the great cat and an extreme tension. The tiger was bursting with raw anger that seemed to swell and grow.

Pepe stopped in his tracks and cold fear crept up his spine. But he did not give way to fear. With deliberate, studied slowness he brought the rifle to his shoulder and took aim. He had only one bullet and there would be no time to reload, but even a tiger could not withstand the smash of that enormous leaden ball right between the eyes. Pepe steadied the rifle.

His finger tightened slowly on the trigger, for he must not let nervousness spoil his aim. When the hammer fell Pepe's brain and body became momentarily numb.

There was no satisfying roar and no puff of black powder smoke wafting away from the muzzle. Instead there was only a sudden hiss, as though cold water had spilled on a hot stone, and the metallic click of the falling hammer. Pepe himself had loaded the rifle, but he could not have done so correctly. Only the powder in the priming pan flashed.

It was the spark needed to explode the anger in the tiger's lithe and deadly body. He emitted a coughing snarl and launched his charge. Lord of the jungle, he would crush this puny man who dared interfere with him.

Pepe jerked back to reality, but he took time to think of his rifle, leaning it lovingly against a tree and in the same motion jerking his machete from its sheath.

It was now a hopeless fight, to be decided in the tiger's favor, because not within the memory of the village's oldest inhabitant had any man ever killed a tiger with a machete. But it was as well to fight hopelessly, as to turn and run, for if he did that he would surely be killed. No tiger that attacked anything was ever known to turn aside.

Machete in hand, Pepe studied the onrushing cat. He had read the tracks correctly, for from pad to joint the tiger's right front foot was swollen to almost twice the size of the other. It must have stepped on a poisonous thorn or been bitten by a snake.

Even with such a handicap, a tiger was more than a match for a man armed only with a machete—but Pepe watched the right front paw carefully. If he had any advantage, it lay there. Then the tiger, a terrible, pitiless engine of destruction, flung himself at Pepe. Pepe had known from the first that the tiger's initial strike would be exactly this one, and he was ready for it. He swerved, bending his body outward as the great cat brushed past him. With all the strength in his powerful right arm, he swung the machete. He stopped his downward stroke just short of the tiger's silken back, for he knew suddenly that there was just one way to end this fight.

The tiger whirled, and hot spittle from his mouth splashed on the back of Pepe's left hand. Holding the machete before him, like a sword, he took a swift backward step. The tiger sprang, launching himself from the ground as though his rear legs were made of powerful steel springs, and coming straight up. His flailing left paw flashed at Pepe. It hooked in his shirt, ripping it away from the arm as though it were paper, and burning talons sank into the flesh. Red blood welled out.

Pepe did not try again to slash with the machete, but thrust, as he would have thrust with a knife or sword. The machete's point met the tiger's throat, and Pepe put all his strength and weight behind it. The blade explored its way into living flesh, and the tiger gasped. Blood bubbled over the machete.

With a convulsive effort, the tiger pulled himself away. But blood was rushing from his throat now and he shook his head, then stumbled and fell. He pulled himself erect, looked with glazing eyes at Pepe and dragged himself toward him. There was a throttled snarl. The tiger slumped to the ground. The tip of his tail twitched and was still.

Pepe stared, scarcely seeing the blood that flowed from his lacerated arm. He had done the impossible, he had killed a tiger with a machete. Pepe brushed a hand across his eyes and took a trembling forward step.

He picked up his rifle and looked again to the priming. There seemed to be nothing wrong. Repriming, Pepe clasped the rifle with his elbow and seized the machete's hilt. Bracing one foot against the tiger's head, he drew the machete out.

Then he held his rifle so close to the machete wound that the muzzle caressed silken fur. He pulled the trigger. The wound gaped wider and smoke-blackened fur fringed it. All traces of the machete wound were obliterated. Pepe knew a second's anguished regret, then steeled himself, for this was the way it must be.

Everybody had a machete. In his village, the man who owned a rifle must remain supreme.

About the author

Jim Kjelgaard (1910–1959) grew up on a farm in Tioga County in the Pennsylvania mountain region. It was a wonderful place for a boy because of the abundance of fish and game in the region. Here Kjelgaard acquired his great love of the outdoor life. Many of his books reflect this love of hunting, and trapping and forest lore. It was almost a process of elimination that brought Kjelgaard to writing. Earlier, he had tried his hand as a laborer, a teamster, a factory worker, a plumber's apprentice, and as a surveyor's assistant. Among his other books are *Big Red*, *Red Siege*, and *Forest Patrol*.

Questions for discussion

1. Is Pepe an admirable character? Give reasons and examples to support your answer.
2. Pepe had to choose between being hailed as a courageous hero, and being "master" of his village. In what way was he master of the village? What were the reasons for his choice?
3. If Pepe had told the villagers what had really happened, what admission would he have had to make about the gun? What would this admission have done to his position in the village?
4. The gun did two things for Pepe. It gave him a satisfying way of earning a living. What else?
5. What evidence is there that Pepe was shrewd and crafty? That he was superstitious? What kind of person was Pepe? Look carefully at the picture of him (a) before the tiger arrived (b) while he waited for Juan (c) while bargaining with Juan (d) while in the forest.
6. Pepe had it in his power to rid the natives of their superstitious beliefs about "tigers and devils." He chose not to. Why? What does this tell you about Pepe's character?
7. ". . . not within the memory of the village's oldest inhabitants had any man ever killed a tiger with a machete." The whole story turns upon the fact stated in this sentence. Why is it so important to the story?
8. Were you surprised by the ending of the story? Show how the author prepared you for this ending. What clues does he give you about Pepe, his regard for the gun, and the reasons for his using it?
9. Does Pepe's victory over the tiger seem reasonable as you read it? What does the author tell you about Pepe that makes the outcome of the fight more believable?

Vocabulary growth

WORDS ARE INTERESTING. The word *eerie* has an interesting history. Originally it meant "timid, or cowardly." Thus, it was a term applied to persons and animals. Later, the word came to mean "inspiring fear, weird, uncanny." The aspect of cowardice is no longer present in the word. Note its use in the second sentence of the story, " . . . an eerie silence enveloped the thatched village." Reread the next four sentences to see how they build meaning into the word *eerie*. By the way, you will be interested to see what the dictionary tells you about *uncanny*.

CONTEXT. Use the context clues to discover the meaning of the unfamiliar words which appear in the following sentences:

a. On page 45, read the sentence, "They used machetes . . ." What clue tells you what a *machete* is?

b. What do you learn about *papaya* from this sentence? "Then he . . . breakfasted on a papaya he had gathered the day before."

c. On page 47, read the sentence, "Only death would end his forays." Read the rest of the paragraph and explain the meaning of *forays*.

For composition

Reread the first two paragraphs. Can you feel with the natives the fear of the mysterious and unknown? Note the sentence, "Because it was a time of the unknown, night had to be a time of fear." Do people fear the unknown more than the known? Do superstitions arise out of the unknown? Do people today have any fear about ominous dangers? Do people today have any superstitions about science itself? Write a composition on the topic "Superstitions of Our Time" or "What Modern Man Fears."

The Tell-Tale Heart

EDGAR ALLAN POE

The man denies that he is insane. He offers proof. Can you believe him?

TRUE! nervous—very, very dreadfully nervous I had been and am; but why *will* you say that I am mad? The disease had sharpened my senses—not destroyed—not dulled them. Above all was the sense of hearing acute. I heard all things in the heaven and in the earth. I heard many things in hell. How, then, am I mad? Hearken! and observe how healthily—how calmly I can tell you the whole story.

It is impossible to say how first the idea entered my brain; but once conceived, it haunted me day and night. Object there was none. Passion there was none. I loved the old man. He had never wronged me. He had never given me insult. For his gold I had no desire. I think it was his eye! yes, it was this! He had the eye of a vulture —a pale blue eye, with a film over it. Whenever it fell upon me, my blood ran cold; and so by degrees—very gradually—I made up my mind to take the life of the old man, and thus rid myself of the eye forever.

Now this is the point. You fancy me mad. Madmen know nothing. But you should have seen *me*. You should have seen how wisely I proceeded—with what caution—with what foresight—with what dissimulation I went to work! I was never kinder to the old man than during the whole week before I killed him. And every night, about midnight, I turned the latch of his door and opened it—ah, so gently! And then, when I had made an opening sufficient for my head, I put in a dark lantern, all closed, closed, so that no light shone out, and then I thrust in my head. Oh, you would have laughed to see how cunningly I thrust it in! I moved it slowly—very, very slowly, so that I might not disturb the old man's sleep. It took me an hour to place my whole head within the opening so far that I could see him as he lay upon his bed. Ha!—would a madman have been so wise as this? And then, when my head was well in the room, I undid the lantern cautiously—oh, so cautiously—cautiously (for the hinges creaked) —I undid it just so much that a single thin ray fell upon the vulture eye. And this I did for seven long nights—every night just at midnight—but I found the eye always closed; and so it was impossible to do the work; for it was not the old man who vexed me, but his Evil Eye. And every morning, when the day broke, I went boldly into the chamber, and spoke courageously to him, calling him by name in a hearty tone, and inquiring how he had passed the night. So you see he would have been a very profound old man, indeed, to suspect that every night, just at twelve, I looked in upon him while he slept.

Upon the eighth night I was more than usually cautious in opening the door. A watch's minute hand moves more quickly than did mine. Never, before that night, had I *felt* the extent of my own powers—of my sagacity. I could scarcely contain my feelings of triumph. To think that there I was, opening the door, little by little, and he not even to dream of my secret deeds or thoughts. I fairly chuckled at the idea; and perhaps he heard me; for he moved on the bed suddenly, as if startled. Now you may think that I drew back —but no. His room was as black as pitch with the thick darkness (for the shutters were close fastened, through fear of robbers), and so I knew that he could not see the opening of the door, and I kept pushing it on steadily, steadily.

I had my head in, and was about to open the lantern, when my thumb slipped upon the tin fastening, and the old man sprang up in bed, crying out, "Who's there?"

I kept quite still and said nothing. For a whole hour I did not move a muscle, and in the meantime I did not hear him lie down. He was still sitting up in the bed listening—just as I have done, night after night, hearkening to the death watches in the wall.

Presently I heard a slight groan, and I knew it was the groan of mortal terror. It was not a groan of pain or of grief—oh, no!—it was the low stifled sound that arises from the bottom of the soul when overcharged with awe. I knew the sound well. Many a night, just at midnight, when all the world slept, it has welled up from my own bosom, deepening, with its dreadful echo, the terrors that distracted me. I say I knew it well. I knew what the old man felt, and pitied him, although I chuckled at heart. I knew that he had been lying awake ever since the first slight noise, when he had turned in his bed. His fears had been ever since growing upon him. He had been trying to fancy them causeless, but could not. He had been saying to himself—"It is nothing but the wind in the chimney—it is only a mouse crossing the floor," or "It is merely a cricket which has made a single chirp." Yes, he had been trying to comfort himself with these suppositions: but he had found all in vain. *All in vain*; because Death, in approaching him, had stalked with his black shadow before him, and enveloped the victim. And it was the mournful influence of the unperceived shadow that caused him to feel—although he neither saw nor heard—to *feel* the presence of my head within the room.

When I had waited a long time, very patiently, without hearing him lie down, I resolved to open a little—a very, very little crevice in the lantern. So I opened it—you cannot imagine how stealthily, stealthily—until at length a single dim ray, like the thread of the spider, shot from out the crevice and fell upon the vulture eye.

It was open—wide, wide open—and I grew furious as I gazed upon it. I saw it with perfect distinctiveness—all a dull blue, with a hideous veil over it that chilled the very marrow in my bones; but I could see nothing else of the old man's face or person; for I had directed the ray as if by instinct, precisely upon the damned spot.

And have I not told you that what you mistake for madness is but overacuteness of the senses?—Now, I say, there came to my ears a low, dull, quick sound, such as a watch makes when enveloped in cotton. I knew *that* sound well, too. It was the beating of the old man's heart. It increased my fury, as the beating of a drum stimulates the soldier into courage.

But even yet I refrained and kept still. I scarcely breathed. I held the lantern motionless. I tried how steadily I could maintain the ray upon the eye. Meantime the hellish tattoo of the heart increased. It grew quicker and quicker, and louder and louder every instant. The old man's terror *must* have been extreme! It grew louder, I say, louder every moment!—do you mark me well? I have told you that I am nervous: so I am. And now at the dead hour of the night, amid the dreadful silence of that old house, so strange a noise as this excited me to uncontrollable terror. Yet, for some minutes longer I refrained and stood still. But the beating grew louder, louder!

I thought the heart must burst. And now a new anxiety seized me
—the sound would be heard by a neighbor! The old man's hour had
come! With a loud yell, I threw open the lantern and leaped into
the room. He shrieked once—once only. In an instant I dragged him
to the floor, and pulled the heavy bed over him. I then smiled gaily,
to find the deed so far done. But, for many minutes, the heart beat
on with a muffled sound. This, however, did not vex me; it would not
be heard through the wall. At length it ceased. The old man was
dead. I removed the bed and examined the corpse. Yes, he was stone,
stone dead. I placed my hand upon the heart and held it there many
minutes. There was no pulsation. He was stone dead. His eye would
trouble me no more.

If still you think me mad, you will think so no longer when I
describe the wise precautions I took for the concealment of the body.
The night waned, and I worked hastily, but in silence. First of all
I dismembered the corpse. I cut off the head and the arms and
the legs.

I then took up three planks from the flooring of the chamber,
and deposited all between the scantlings. I then replaced the boards
so cleverly, so cunningly, that no human eye—not even *his*—could
have detected anything wrong. There was nothing to wash out—no
stain of any kind—no blood spot whatever. I had been too wary for
that. A tub had caught all—ha! ha!

When I had made an end of these labors, it was four o'clock—
still dark as midnight. As the bell sounded the hour, there came a
knocking at the street door. I went down to open it with a light heart
—for what had I *now* to fear? There entered three men, who introduced themselves, with perfect suavity, as officers of the police.
A shriek had been heard by a neighbor during the night; suspicion
of foul play had been aroused; information had been lodged at the
police office, and they (the officers) had been deputed to search
the premises.

I smiled—for *what* had I to fear? I bade the gentlemen welcome.
The shriek, I said, was my own in a dream. The old man, I mentioned, was absent in the country. I took my visitors all over the
house. I bade them search—search *well*. I led them, at length, to *his*
chamber. I showed them his treasures, secure, undisturbed. In the
enthusiasm of my confidence, I brought chairs into the room, and
desired them *here* to rest from their fatigues, while I myself, in the

wild audacity of my perfect triumph, placed my own seat upon the very spot beneath which reposed the corpse of the victim.

The officers were satisfied. My *manner* had convinced them. I was singularly at ease. They sat, and while I answered cheerily, they chatted of familiar things. But, erelong, I felt myself getting pale and wished them gone. My head ached, and I fancied a ringing in my ears: but still they sat and still they chatted. The ringing became more distinct—it continued and became more distinct; I talked more freely to get rid of the feeling; but it continued and gained definiteness—until, at length, I found that the noise was *not* within my ears.

No doubt I now grew *very* pale—but I talked more fluently, and with a heightened voice. Yet the sound increased—and what could I do? It was *a low, dull, quick sound—much such a sound as a watch makes when enveloped in cotton.* I gasped for breath—and yet the officers heard it not. I talked more quickly—more vehemently; but the noise steadily increased. I arose and argued about trifles, in a high key and with violent gesticulations; but the noise steadily increased. Why *would* they not be gone? I paced the floor to and fro with heavy strides, as if excited to fury by the observations of the men—but the noise steadily increased. Oh, God! what *could* I do? I foamed—I raved—I swore! I swung the chair upon which I had been sitting, and grated it upon the boards, but the noise arose over all and continually increased. It grew louder—louder—*louder!* And still the men chatted pleasantly, and smiled. Was it possible they heard not? Almighty God!—no, no! They heard!—they suspected!— they *knew!*—they were making a mockery of my horror!—this I thought, and this I think. But anything was better than this agony! Anything was more tolerable than this derision! I could bear those hypocritical smiles no longer! I felt that I must scream or die! and now—again!—hark! louder! louder! louder! *louder!*

"Villains!" I shrieked, "dissemble no more! I admit the deed! —tear up the planks! here, here!—it is the beating of his hideous heart!"

About the author

Edgar Allan Poe (1809–1849) is today regarded by some scholars as the most important American poet of the first half of the nineteenth century. He was also a leading pioneer in the field of the short story. Poe's brief life was a hectic and tragic one. At one point, he trained for a military career at West Point. Finding this life unsuitable, he turned to writing, and spent the rest of his life as either a contributor to, or an editor of, various magazines. One of his most significant contributions to literature is his clearly defined theory of the short story. In each of his stories, he aimed for singleness of effect, and made all other considerations secondary.

Questions for discussion

1. Here is the story of a man who had committed "a perfect crime." Were you disappointed when he confessed? If so, how would you have ended the story?

2. You have read several stories in which there is a surprise ending. You have learned how important it is for the writer to plant clues that later make the surprise solution seem reasonable. The writer of a detective or crime story has this same obligation. But he must hide the outcome of his story from the reader until the last possible moment.

   At what point is the outcome of "The Tell-Tale Heart" first disclosed? Does the writer give away the outcome before it occurs? What do you know about the man that makes it reasonable for him to confess? Are there any incidents in the story that seem unreasonable, improbable, or not likely? Why does the man emphasize in the first paragraph and later that his sense of hearing is acute?

3. In most detective stories, the reader's problem is to find out who the criminal is. In "The Tell-Tale Heart" the criminal is known. Your problem is to find out *how* and *why* he was caught. How was the man in this story caught? Why did he confess? Which incidents in the story surprised you as you read them?

4. In most detective stories, the writer spends little time in telling how the crime was committed. How many paragraphs of "The Tell-Tale Heart" actually tell of the crime? Why are so many details of the crime given? Which of these details is the most horrifying? Why does the writer use the expression "ha-ha!" on page 57? Which details especially amused the murderer as he told of his crime? What two things cause the man of the story to feel horror and fear?

5. The entire story is a murderer's account of his crime. Throughout, he is trying to justify his actions. In what way does his account differ from a confession? Does he express any horror or disgust for what he has done? What reason does the man have for telling the story? What is he trying to prove? What evidence does the man offer to prove that he is not mad? What is the effect on the reader of the man's repeated assertion that he is not mad?

6. As the story progresses, the reader can see a conflict between the murderer's confidence and his fear. At what point does his fear make him over-cautious? At what point does his confidence become over-confidence? How does over-confidence lead to his downfall? How does the man interpret the actions of the police at the end of the story? At what point do the police know he has killed the old man?

7. Murder under any circumstances is shocking, but murder by a madman has a special horror because it is without reason, and because it cannot be predicted. Which of the murderer's reactions seem to be especially those of a sick mind? Why did the murderer stand for an hour in the old man's bedroom? What was the effect of this waiting upon the old man? What effect did the old man's terror have upon the murderer? How does the writer show the fears and terrors of the mentally-ill person in this story?

8. The *theme* of a story is its basic idea. The theme is what the story is about. The theme is never stated in terms of the action of the story. The theme of "The Tell-Tale Heart" is not murder. The story is not about the murder of an old man by a mentally-ill person. Can you state the theme of "The Tell-Tale Heart"?

9. ATMOSPHERE. A room or a house has an atmosphere of friendliness, or of gloom, of mystery, or even of terror. The atmosphere of a place is the impression it creates in you or the feelings that it arouses. Impressions and feelings are determined by physical details that strike our senses—darkness, light, color, noise or silence, and so on. In a similar way, a story may have an atmosphere about it. The atmosphere is deliberately created by the writer through his choice of details—details that appeal to our senses. In "The Tell-Tale Heart," for example, the atmosphere is created not only by the details presented by the madman, but by the manner in which he speaks. Even the strange quiet of the police contributes to your feelings, and to the overall impression the story makes upon you.

    The same words that are used to describe the atmosphere of a room or a house—warmth, friendliness, horror, gloom, can be used to describe the atmosphere of a story.

    a. What one word sums up the atmosphere of "The Tell-Tale Heart"?

    b. What details of the story help to create this atmosphere?

Vocabulary growth

WORDS ARE INTERESTING. Did you notice the interesting words in this story?

vex. This comes from a Latin word meaning "to shake or agitate."

Today *vex* means "to make trouble for; disturb; annoy." Do you see how the old Latin meaning carries over into modern usage?

hearty. You will find it interesting to note how many words and phrases are based upon names of parts of the body: *head, hand, foot, face,* etc. You know the functions of the suffix *-y*. Do you know these expressions: *break one's heart, do one's heart good, eat one's heart out, have a heart, wear one's heart?* Are you sure you know what they mean? Now look up the meaning of *hearty* in your dictionary.

agony. This word goes back to ancient Greek times. In those days an *agonia* was a contest for victory. See how the word is used in the sixth line from the last in this story.

wane. This word goes back a thousand years to an Anglo-Saxon word meaning "to decrease, grow less." *Wane* is closely related to the word *want*. The opposite, or antonym, of *wane* is *wax*. If *wane* means "to grow less," what does *wax* mean? Curiously enough, *wax* is closely related to *waist*, which is the part of the body between the ribs and the hips. No · doubt the word *waist* was invented by some middle-aged gentleman who observed sadly the effect of much good food upon his figure.

WORD PARTS. The suffixes *-ful* and *-ous* are used to make adjectives from nouns. They add meaning to the words in which they appear: *full of, having the qualities of, pertaining to.* You see these suffixes in *cautious, nervous, dreadful,* on pages 54–55. Work out the meaning of these words, using the meanings of the suffixes. Look for other words on the same pages with these suffixes.

For composition

1. This story is told in the first person. Rewrite the first two paragraphs in the third person to see how it changes. You might begin:
     "True! nervous—very, very dreadfully nervous he had been and is; but why *will* you say he is mad? The disease had sharpened his senses . . ."
2. Write the report turned in by the policeman which recounts his experiences from the moment he received the neighbor's call about a shriek in the dark.
3. Everyone has had moments of great anguish. This anguish may have been caused by any number of things—embarrassment, fear, anxiety, or sorrow, to name just a few. Write a paragraph in which you attempt to describe your feelings during such an experience.

Susana and the Shepherd

MARGARET CRAVEN

You will know more about our country and more about people when you have seen them through the eyes of Juan Varra. In the lonely mountain highlands, he grazes the Americano's flocks, and in the lowlands, nearer civilization, where the sheep are wintered, he meets friends. And if one of the friends is Susana, who knows—?

ALL the passengers on the big transcontinental plane were interested in the young Basque who occupied the rear seat. He was a good-looking lad with his dark eyes and his proud, inscrutable face, tagged on the jacket with a check badge like a piece of luggage because he couldn't speak an English word.

"He's a sheepherder from the Spanish Pyrenees," the stewardess replied to an inquiry. "The California Range Association is flying over many of them. Usually three or four come together. He's the first to come alone."

Several of the passengers tried to be friendly, but the young Basque only stared at them, too bewildered and confused to smile, and finally a sure blonde, who had traveled in Spain, said she'd draw him out. She'd toss a little Spanish at him. She'd just go over and sit on the arm of his chair and give him the good old American *bienvenida.*

So she did it, and the young Basque fixed upon her a pair of scornful, suspicious eyes and ignored her.

"You know what I think?" said the defeated blonde to the stewardess. "I think his mother warned him to have nothing to do with American women. They'd eat him alive." And she was wrong; it was his grandmother who had warned him.

"Oh, he's a strange one," the stewardess told the navigator.

"They're all silent, but this one wouldn't even talk if he knew how. I hope somebody meets him in San Francisco. I have strict orders not to turn him loose unless he's met."

The navigator was wiser. "He's from some small village, probably," he said. "Never seen a big city. Never been in a plane. If he's afraid, it's the kind of fear only the brave know. Otherwise he wouldn't be crossing an ocean and a continent to herd sheep for a stranger in a land he doesn't know. Let him alone. He's a kid with a dream."

And after that, across the plains and the mountains, the boy sat undisturbed, holding his dream, and his was the old dream many Basque boys have held in their hearts. Their land was not big or rich enough to support all. By custom, a family's land was left to the eldest son. The younger sons, therefore, must emigrate; their only hope of keeping the land they loved was to leave it—and come back rich.

It was possible. From his own village in the Valle de Arce in the province of Navarra several had done it. Felipe Lacabe had done it. He had herded sheep for six years in a place called Nevada. In all that time he had learned no more than fifty English words, and been to town twice, and spent not one coin on drink, smokes and girls. He had come back with twelve thousand dollars—a fabulous fortune—and he had bought himself a band of fine sheep and married the prettiest girl in Uriz.

Many had come back, and more had not. Whenever American tourists came to the remote villages of the Pyrenees some Basque father, prodded by his wife, said slowly, "If you have been to California, is it possible you know our son, Bonifacio?" or Fermín. Or Esteban. But they never did.

He, Juan Varra, was going to be one of the lucky ones. He had made up his mind. The American consul at Bilbao before whom he had appeared for his sheepherder's examination had praised him. The doctor who had given him his physical had spoken of his strength. And while he had waited the long months for the completion of his papers, the priest had strengthened him.

No Basque had ever been remembered for his words, the priest had said. Only for deeds and for courage. And if the ignorant thought he had a mist in his head like the mists of the mountains he loved, what of it? The thing to do was to be strong.

Yet when it was almost time to land, the boy found it hard to be strong. He reminded himself that an unknown *Americano* had paid seven hundred and eleven dollars and ten cents for his passage, sight unseen, and why? Because he knew—as who does not?—that for two thousand years the Basques have been famous for their skill with the sheep.

He thought hard on *abuelita*, his little grandmother. How confidently she had smiled at him as she had prepared his favorite omelet for his last supper at home. With no teeth, she had looked like a little old baby, and he vowed now that with his first wages he would send her enough money to buy a set of shiny white store teeth, so she could walk through the village, head high and smiling.

Also he thought of his little brother, who had begged to come along, who must emigrate, too, when he was older. He must set him an example. He must not fail.

Then the plane landed. The passengers began to file out slowly. He followed them. Surely el Cid, the bravest knight in all Christendom, never went forth to battle more stanchly than Juan Varra left that plane, the little stewardess at his heels, praying fervently somebody would meet him and ready to grab his jacket tails if no one did.

He was the last to pass the gate, and as he stepped through he saw the most beautiful sight possible to any Basque far from home. He saw another Basque. He saw a browned face, no longer young, which was smiling and showing some splendid gold teeth. And the voice was speaking his own dialect and it said, "Welcome, Juan Varra, and are the girls still as pretty in Navarra?" And this was Ancelito, thirty years from home and as much of a Basque as ever.

Ancelito collected his luggage and led him to the pickup truck. When they had left the confusion of the city, and were driving through the great wide green Sacramento Valley, Ancelito dropped pleasantries and began to speak so slowly and seriously in Spanish that the boy knew he must remember every word.

Now in early May the alfilaria was already dry. The corkscrew spirals on the wild grass that can work their way into the sheep's hides had already formed. It was vital, therefore, that the sheep be moved at once from the low range. Separated into bands, sheared and branded, they had been driven to a central campsite, the trailer houses of the herders accompanying them. At the campsite, freight cars waited. The rich *Americano* who owned the sheep had rented a whole train, and this very moment he was supervising the loading of the sheep bands into the cars. Tonight the train would carry the sheep across the great mountains into Nevada, where the long summer drive would begin at dawn.

Usually, said Ancelito, a youngster from the homeland was kept on the valley ranch for several weeks to accustom him to the strange American ways. But now they were desperate for herders. Last year they had lost two older men from heart attacks. The camp tender had found them at eight thousand feet, stiff in their blankets. It would be necessary for Juan Varra to go with them to Nevada and to start out at dawn with a band of two thousand sheep. Every other day a camp tender would bring him supplies and tell him where to find water. He would have a burro, of course, and a dog which Ancelito, himself, had trained.

"There is nothing to fear," Ancelito told him gravely. "The dog will know what you do not."

The boy said with dignity, "I have no fear."

Ancelito questioned him carefully, and in response the boy told him, shyly and briefly, a little of his dream. After four hours' driving, they came at last to the campsite.

In the trailer house Juan Varra ate a quick meal while Ancelito checked the clothes and the bedding he'd need. Then it was time to go, and they walked together through the dark to the train.

"You will go in the caboose," said Ancelito. "You will sleep better, and tomorrow you will need that sleep. I will go by truck with the others, and I will see you at daybreak."

Once, at night in his bunk, the boy woke and felt the train moving under him and the cold air on his cheek, and he could hear the hard pull of the engine, and knew they were crossing the mountains. When he woke again, it was to the smell of coffee and the touch of a trainman's hand on his shoulder. He put on his shoes and his jacket and drank two cups of coffee. When he left the caboose, he stepped out into the clear dawn and such a sight as he had never seen.

Already the sheep were being spilled out into the sage, each band at a time, its loaded burro, herder and dog waiting to drive it away.

Because he was new, his band was the last. Then it, too, was spilled into the sage, and his burro and dog and a sheep tender drove the band away from the tracks as Ancelito motioned him to wait.

The train moved on, the boy waiting by the truck while Ancelito talked earnestly to the *Americano* who owned the sheep, and though they spoke English and the boy could not understand a word, he knew the *Americano* was worried.

"Andy, I'm scared to death to send him out. Can he do it?"

"Yes. He's used to hardship. He is not an American boy. He does not put his manhood in a car that can go ninety miles an hour. It is in himself."

"I know. He'll have the inbred willingness to endure."

"He has something else. He has a dream."

"All right. Let him go."

Then Ancelito gave the boy his directions and told him where he would find water. The owner shook his hand.

Juan ran into the sage and took the crook from the tender, and he gave the old signal to the dog with a lift of his hand and he was off and on his own. He did not permit himself to look back for some moments. When he did so, it was as if the truck, the men, the other bands of sheep had never existed, so quickly had the land taken them. And it was unlike any land he had ever seen, and vaster than any he had ever imagined.

The sage and the green buckbrush stretched as endlessly as eternity, broken only by a few small yellow sunflowers and a very occasional pine. No friendly villages. No small white houses with cheerful red-tiled roofs. Nothing but mountains which did not stand up proudly as mountains should, but lay rolling beneath his old high shoes.

He could scarcely bear to look at the sheep, so great was his disappointment. How ugly they were with their strange snub-nosed faces. The factory-made crook was awkward to his hand, and so long that he was sure he would never be able to trip a ewe neatly by her hind leg. Even the motley-colored Australian shepherd was unlike any dog he had known.

But the burro was the same. It trudged along with the sheep, carrying his supplies, topped by his big square bedroll. And the sheep baaed like sheep. The lambs frolicked like the lambs at home. And the dog let the sheep scatter only so far, rounding in the strays, circling watchfully.

He counted the black sheep—the markers—carefully. There were twenty-one. He counted the bellwethers. At the nooning-up he would unpack the burro, check his supplies and repack in his own precise way. He would make a fire and set a pot of beans to simmer, and cook himself a meal of ham and eggs. And this night when the coyotes yapped and the dog answered them, prowling the bed grounds, thoughts of home would creep to his little tent and he would begin the long battle against loneliness. And he swore now, by all the lady saints and the gentleman saints in the entire heaven, that he would fight it each night until he won.

It took him six weeks. He had no calendar and no watch, and he needed neither. Each day followed the familiar pattern. He was up before daylight, building his fire beneath the heavy U-shaped iron, brewing his coffee. When the burro was packed, the daily trek began, the sheep scattering over a mile, the boy following, his beat-up .30-.30 in a sling on his back, the dog circling, alert to every sound of his voice, every movement of his hands.

Each nooning-up Juan cooked his meal while the sheep lay in the sage, chewing their cud. And every other day the sheep tender came bumping through the buckbrush in his four-wheel-drive truck, bringing fresh meat and food, even water if necessary, and an eight-pound round loaf of white Basque bread which he had baked in a long pit. The sheep tender was a Basque also, but he had been too long alone. He had lost his dream. He could not talk easily to anyone, and when he spoke, it was always of some café called Estrellita or Española in some valley town where he could fill himself up on red wine, poured from a goatskin, and eat prodigiously.

Sometimes on the rainy nights when the coyotes cried like women, the boy was so homesick for his land and his people that it was an agony within him, and he rose shaken and white. He dreamed one night of his *abuelita*, smiling and showing her toothless gums, and when he awoke, his cheeks were wet, and though never for an instant did he admit it was from anything but rain leaking in the tent, after that he felt better.

Gradually the sheep did not seem quite so snub-nosed and ugly. They became the familiar sheep. He knew them, and a few too well —especially the cantankerous ewe with the twin lambs which he called "*La Bruja*," the witch. He grew fond of his burro, and he loved the dog as deeply as a man can love a friend.

Then the six weeks were over, and with his band he took the old trail toward the higher mountains, the little burro leading the way because it knew it well. They reached the river, followed and forded it into the great national forest, traveling twenty miles in three days into the juniper range.

They were in the juniper forest a week, working their way up to the ponderosa and the sugar pine, and here the boy's loneliness left him. Often he saw deer browsing at dawn and dusk; a doe keeping herself carefully between him and her fawn. Once, in the early evening when the sheep had settled for the night, he came on a mother bear, scolding, slapping and cuffing her two cubs to hurry them out of his way. Even the birds were a delight, the mountain bluebirds and jays, the sap-suckers and the black-and-yellow orioles. Here he was no longer a boy far from home. He was a Basque herder at his best, responsible and resourceful, like a soldier at some lonely outpost.

The tender's truck could not follow them now. The *Americano* who owned the sheep had established two cabins at seventy-five hundred feet from which several tenders took supplies to the various sheep bands by pack mule. And when Juan saw Ancelito riding through the trees leading a mule he laughed aloud, startled by the sound of his own voice.

The mule was a walking grocery, its pack bags heavy with flour sacks, each fat with supplies.

Then for the first time Juan Varra was afraid. He was so afraid he wanted to bolt like *La Bruja*, the witch ewe. On the mule bringing up the rear was a girl.

Ancelito dismounted. . . . Had it gone well? . . . Yes. . . . Had he been lonely? . . . No—perhaps a very little at first. And as he spoke not once did the boy glance at the girl.

It was only Susana, said Ancelito; and she was his daughter, come to the cabins for a few days, as he had promised her. She was quite harmless. As women go, she was no trouble. She would get the noon meal while they unpacked the supplies.

And she did. While the boy and Ancelito unpacked the supplies and discussed the best sites for the bed grounds and the danger of bears, Juan could hear the girl moving at the fire.

When the meal was ready and they sat down for slabs of jack cheese, ham and eggs, fresh bread and coffee, he was forced to look at her. Her feet were as big as a boy's. Her legs were encased in thick blue cotton pants like a boy's. Her top half was submerged in a shirt like a boy's. Her hair was drawn tight to the back of her head, and hung in a thick brush, suitable only for a horse's tail. Furthermore, she did not look up at him from under her lashes and touch him with the briefest of cool, sweet glances to tell him she saw every single thing about him and found it good. She looked straight at him, and boldly, as one boy takes the measure of another.

He did not direct to her one word. When the meal was over and Ancelito and his daughter were mounted and leaving, he cast an *"adiós"* into the air, which she could take to include her if she wished.

"Is he alive?" Susana asked her father, when the mules had started.

"Yes."

"Is he stupid?"

"No. He is silent. He is a Basque. I am a Basque."

"When you came to this country you were not like that."

"I was exactly like that. He is afraid of you. But do not worry. I have told him you are harmless."

"Father, you didn't."

"But certainly. It would do you no good to make eyes at this one. He has a dream. He will save his money. He will go back to his village a *millonario* and marry the most beautiful girl in all Navarra. Now, if you were as wise as your mother——"

"Papacito," said Susana slowly, "are the girls so pretty in Navarra?"

And Ancelito smiled at her and said, "Beyond description."

The voices carried back to the boy in the high clear air, and though they were in English, he did not miss the scorn in the girl's voice. That night among the supplies he found that Ancelito had left him a beginner's Spanish-English reader.

Love may need no words, but resentment can use several. The next day Juan Varra opened the first crack in the dark tomb in which he was determined to bury himself for six years. He began to learn to read English.

Two days later, when the grocery mule came through the trees, the boy put on his most proud and silent Basque face, lest the girl think he was glad to see her. But it was not Ancelito and Susana who followed the mule. It was the dull camp tender who had lost his dream.

Juan did not admit to disappointment. He had no time to think of girls. The bears were troublesome. One old killer bear followed the sheep band, killing a ewe each night, and the boy tracked him and shot him. In all, he killed four bears.

In July the rams were brought in, and in August all the sheep bands were driven to a mountain valley, where the ewes were culled, the lambs separated into the fats and the feeders. On the way back to the high range with his reassembled band, Juan passed his first campers, and they were friendly. A little boy chased the lambs and couldn't catch them. The father gave him cigarettes, and the wife smiled at him and made him a present of a kitten.

After that, the cat followed along with the sheep, and though Juan told himself he kept her only to keep the chipmunks from his food, he carried her under his jacket in the thunderstorms, and let her sleep at the foot of his bedroll.

Then, in October, the long drive was done. The sheep were carried by two- and three-decker trucks down from the mountains to the low delta to browse on the corn stubble; the burro was left behind, a cook wagon carrying supplies. Just before Christmas the bands were driven to the home ranch to wait for the lambing, and it was here, in a neat white house, that Ancelito, the foreman, lived with Susana. The boy did not ask for her.

"Am I rich yet?" he asked Ancelito anxiously.

"In this country you are poor as a thin mouse," said Ancelito. "But at home already you can buy the finest house in the village."

It was Ancelito who helped him send money to his *abuelita* for the store teeth and presents for the family. It was Ancelito who brought from town the clothes he needed. After that, he spent nothing, and each month the *Americano* who owned the sheep deposited his wages in a savings account in his name. When, at Christmas, the other herders left the trailer houses and drove to town for a fine binge, he did not go. And when he was working with the sheep near the white house and saw something soft and obviously feminine fluttering on the clothesline in the rear, he looked the other way, so tight was the dream still within him.

Right after Christmas the drop band was collected in a big open field and lambing began. Four hundred lambs were born each night, the boy working out in the cold, helping the young ewes that were having trouble with their firstborn, turning the lambs. One early morning the *Americano* was helping put each ewe and her new lamb into a portable *chiquero*, or pen, so she would claim her lamb, and he watched the boy work.

"He is wonderful," he said. "He will save twenty-five per cent more lambs. . . . Andy, we must keep this one."

"I have thought of it," said Ancelito.

The last night of the lambing, through no fault of his own, the boy lost two little lambs, and this, to a Basque herder, is not cause for sadness, but for heartbreak. Ancelito took him to the white house for food and comfort, and there in the warm kitchen waited Susana.

Gone were the boy's shoes, the pants and the horse's tail. She was as shy as a forest creature and as sweet as any young girl in Navarra on her saint's day. She was the daughter of a Basque and she, too, could be silent. She placed the coffee pot before them without a word. and plates of ham and eggs. Then she left them, turning at the door.

"I am so sorry, Juan," and for an instant her glance touched his cheek and was gone.

He did not see her again, because this was the busy time. Lamb tails to be docked. New sheep bands to be formed. The ewes to be sheared and branded, and the winter was gone, and May here again, and the sheep driven to the campsite to go by train to Nevada. And the first year was over, and the cycle began again.

Now repetition had replaced newness, making the second year even lonelier than the first. In the buckbrush, loneliness became an entity, pressing constantly upon him. The boy talked aloud sometimes to the cat and the burro. The dog, of course, was his abiding friend.

Rarely the camp tender brought him letters from home. Those from his *abuelita* and his little brother were the same. They loved him; they missed him. But the letter from his eldest brother, who was head of the family, held a new tone. How fortunate Juan was to be in that land where everyone was rich and all was easy. How hard it was to be the one who was left behind. Oh, he must not stay away too long. If he worked harder and was given a raise—if he saved all beyond the barest necessities, perhaps five years would be enough, or even four.

In the juniper forest one June day he heard a strange little whimpering, crying sound, and came on a lone fawn. He longed to make a pet of it, to keep it with him, as the herders did sometimes. But he could not bear to take it from its mother, to teach it to be unafraid of man, to notch its ear so that when some hunter shot it he would know that once it had had too good a friend in man. It reminded him of the girl.

Then again he had driven the sheep band into the ponderosa and sugar pines of the high range, and he was home in the mountains.

When the grocery mule came through the trees, Ancelito was with it, but not Susana. This time the boy asked for her.

"And how is your daughter?" he asked formally, and Ancelito said she was well. She was going to school this summer. She was educating her head.

"It is that she does not wish a husband?" the boy asked slowly, and Ancelito said that, like all girls, she hoped to find one. But in this country it was the custom for many girls to help their husbands get started. Suppose Susana should marry a man who wished to own a sheep band of his very own. What a fine thing if she could help him. Did Juan know that the sheepman chosen as the year's best in all California was the son of a Basque whose father had come first as a herder? No doubt his wife had helped him, as his mother had helped his father. It was one of the strange American ways.

Several times this year the forest ranger came by at nooning-up and shared his meal. And once a party of mountaineers coming out from a climb passed by and hailed him. He had picked up enough English to say a few words now, but he was alone so much that the sound of a voice always startled him and filled him with uneasiness, because it broke the quiet monotony in which he lived.

Then at last it was fall and he and the sheep were back on the delta, working their way toward the home ranch.

"How rich am I now?" he asked Ancelito, who took out his pencil for a bit of figuring and replied gravely, "In this country you have a modest savings, but in Navarra you are a man of some means. All your relatives are trying to borrow money."

When the sheep band neared the home ranch, the boy watched eagerly for Susana to come home for the holidays from the school she attended, forty miles distant. And one afternoon just before Christmas, while he was working in the big field where the drop band was to be collected for the lambing, he saw her arrive, and the sight filled him with horror.

There was a loud and sudden roar, and into the ranch road from the highway bounced a small, open, ancient and rattletrap car, Susana at the wheel, her legs in jeans, her hair streaming behind her in a horse-tail.

"She goes back and forth to school this way," said Ancelito calmly.

"Scares the sheep. It is amazing what an *Americana* will do to educate her head and get ready to help her husband."

It was cold during this year's lambing, and again Juan worked each night in the big open field with the ewes, and late one night twin lambs lost their mother, arriving in this world so weak that in the morning he and Ancelito carried them to the house and bedded them in the warmth of the kitchen stove.

When the boy had finished working with the lambs and stood up, ready to return to the field, he saw that Susana was watching him quietly, sweet and feminine as she had been when she had prepared breakfast the year before.

"You had a good year, Juan?" she asked in Spanish.

"*Sí.*"

"You were lonely?"

"A Basque is never lonely."

"See, *papacito*, he is afraid of me."

"I am afraid of no one."

"He is afraid of me. He is like the others. He learns nothing. He gives nothing. All he sees in this country is money. All he wants is to grab. He is stupid, *papacito*. He is more stupid than the sheep."

The boy followed Ancelito back to the field.

"She likes you," said Ancelito complacently. "If she did not like you, she would not be so *furiosa*."

One day from the fields Juan saw the little rattletrap car take off down the road, and he knew Susana had gone back to school. He put her resolutely from his mind, and the months slipped by until the sheep bands were driven to the campsite and the second year was done.

The third year was as like the second as the second had been like the first. The loneliness and the constant movement of the sheep. The nooning-up and the bedding-down, and the watchful eye that never forgot to count the bellwethers and the black sheep. The coyotes yapping in the night, and the bears coming in the night, and the cat, the dog and the burro. Only the details differed, and the girl's scornful words, and the thought of the girl was constantly in his mind.

In October, two days before the sheep bands were to leave the mountains, an early blizzard caught them; the snow falling so fast and heavily that they could not be driven out in time. The boy built a fire of green wood, so much smoke would rise to guide the camp tender, and Ancelito saw it and came with horses and men to trample and pack the snow so the sheep could move.

"Am I rich now?" Juan asked, sitting beside Ancelito in the truck on their way down to the delta.

"You are not quite a *millonario*," said Ancelito. "You have a little more than five thousand dollars. In your village it would be a very large sum," and he spoke sadly.

"My work has not been good?" asked the boy. "The *Americano* is not satisfied?"

"He is much pleased. This morning when the sheep were safe from the blizzard, I called Susana to tell him. She says there are many letters for you. When a Basque family takes thus to the pen, the news must be bad."

They rode in silence, not to the corn stubble this time, but to the white house, and when they went into the kitchen, Susana handed his letters to the boy, her eyes big and worried.

They left him to read them alone, and when they returned to the kitchen, he was sitting quietly, the letters spread on the table before him, his face stricken. He did not look up.

"My *abuelita* is dead," he said, and when Ancelito tried to comfort him, he made no response, and when Susana set hot coffee before him, he did not thank her. He was silent as only a Basque can be silent.

"Shall I tell you what is wrong?" asked Ancelito. "Shall I tell you how I know?"

The boy did not answer.

"When I came to this country," said Ancelito, "I spent ten years alone with the sheep. I had a dream also. I thought only of my people and of the day I would return to them. When I did so, I could not stand it. I had forgotten such poverty. Things were bad in my village. Everyone was poor and I was rich, and between us was a wall of jealousy I could not tear down or climb over."

The boy did not look up.

"Have you not seen the wall in these letters? Is not your elder brother already resentful? Does he not complain bitterly of your good fortune?"

The boy was silent.

"I bought my parents the finest house in the village! I paid sixty American dollars for it. I gave them money to care for them, and I came back here where I shall never be rich. It is a friendly country. This is what matters."

"*Papacito*, it is useless!" cried Susana. "He is so stupid! Can you believe it? He does not know we love him of truth. He does not know you feel to him as a man to his own son. Let him save and go back. Let him be rich and miserable. Let him marry the most beautiful girl in all of Navarra. What do I care?" And she sat down at the table and began to cry as only a Basque girl can cry—loud and furiously.

Then the boy looked up. "Is it possible to bring my little brother to this country?" he asked slowly.

"It would take time, but it is possible. He could live with us. He could go to school. Susana could teach him to speak English."

"Is it possible Susana could teach me also? Could she teach me to tell her in English that in the mountains when I am alone with the sheep I do not think of any girl in Navarra? I think of her."

"This she would do gladly."

"Then if I have lost my dream, I can replace it with another. And if I do not return, it is nothing. I am a Basque," said the boy proudly, "and a Basque cannot lose his homeland, because he takes it with him always."

Questions for discussion

1. Why was the Americano willing to spend so much money to employ Juan even though he had never seen the boy?
2. What was Juan's dream? The Americano said that Juan would have "the inbred willingness to endure." Can you find evidence that he was right?
3. If Juan had the willingness to endure, why did he give up his dream? You should find four reasons. Would you say that Juan's giving up his dream was an act of weakness? Why? On the basis of the last few paragraphs, what do you think his "new dream" will be?
4. In what ways was Susana a real Basque as well as a real American?
5. Why was Juan so desperately afraid of American girls? What had his grandmother told him?
6. CONFLICT AND PLOT. In some stories there is a strong conflict between one person and another, or between a person and some part of his environment. In other stories, the conflict is inside the mind and heart of the leading character. When a writer plans his story, he arranges at first for one side to have the advantage, and then the other. At one point the hero seems to be winning; at another, he seems to

be losing. To create suspense, the writer must put difficulties in the hero's way, or there will be no story. The story is the account of how the hero either overcomes these difficulties, or succumbs to them.

The plot of "Susana and the Shepherd" is interesting. The following questions will help you to see it.

    a. Why is Susana's name in the title and not Juan's?

    b. Look at the story from Susana's point of view. What did she want? How was this in conflict with what Juan wanted? What did Juan want?

    c. In the end, Susana got what she wanted because Juan changed his mind about his "dream." Trace the ups and downs of Susana's experience. At what point was she losing? When did she start to win out?

    d. Now look at the story from Juan's point of view. At what point was he winning? At what point was he losing out to Susana? What was the turning point or climax in Juan's loss of his dream?

7. ATMOSPHERE. In the question which dealt with the use of atmosphere in "The Tell-Tale Heart," you learned something about how the author goes about the job of creating atmosphere in his story. The atmosphere of terror in "The Tell-Tale Heart" was produced by the gruesome details of the murder, the wild thoughts and speech of the murderer, and finally by the details of the setting.

In "Susana and the Shepherd" the atmosphere is created by details of the hardships endured, the rigors of Juan's life, and by his silent acceptance of them. Details of the physical setting also contribute to the story's atmosphere.

In speaking of the atmosphere of a story, you can say that it is cheerful, gay, horrible, tense, dramatic, quiet, suspenseful, and so on. The words you choose will reflect the feelings aroused in you by the story.

    a. What feelings did the story arouse in you? What words would you choose to describe its atmosphere?

    b. What details, in particular, contribute to the atmosphere of "Susana and the Shepherd"?

Vocabulary growth

VARIANT MEANINGS. The following sentence, taken from the story, illustrates dramatically the variety of meanings that lie in most English words: "Juan ran into the *sage* and took the *crook* from the *tender*." Look up the italicized words in the dictionary and see how many different meanings you can build into the sentence.

CONTEXT. A sentence acts as context to a word, reinforcing and expanding its meaning. Note how the following sentences throw light on the word *crook* as it is used in the story.

   a. "Juan ran into the sage and took the crook from the tender."
   b. "The factory-made crook was awkward in his hand, and so long that he was sure that he would never be able to trip a ewe neatly by her hind leg."

From these sentences it is possible to see that a *crook* is a tool of some kind, used by sheepherders. It is used to control the movement of sheep in flocks, and it is long.

   c. Find the sentence on page 64 where context reveals the meaning of *abuelita.*
   d. Find the sentences on pages 66 and 67 that tell you the meaning of *nooning-up.*
   e. Find passages which throw light on the meaning of *ewe.*

For composition

1. Write the letter that Juan must write to his older brother, telling him of his change in plans. How would he explain his not returning to Navarra? How would he persuade his older brother to send the younger brother to America?
2. Write an account in dialogue of the moment when Juan asks Susana to help him learn English. Did you notice at the end of the story that Juan spoke to Ancelito, not to Susana? If you know Spanish, you might include Spanish words in your dialogue.
3. What is it like to be alone in a strange country, or even a strange city? If you have had this experience, you might write an account of it, explaining your feelings at the time.

Road to the Isles

JESSAMYN WEST

Everyone is continually making discoveries about himself and about other people. Sometimes these discoveries can come as a shock. On the night of the dance festival, Cress made some important discoveries.

IT was the last Thursday in January, about nine in the evening, cold and raining. The three Delahantys sat close about the living-room fireplace—Mr. Delahanty at the built-in desk working on his schedule, Mrs. Delahanty on the sofa reading, and between them, crosswise in the wing chair, their fourteen-year-old daughter, Crescent. Cress was apparently studying the program of the folk-dance festival in which she was to appear the next evening. For the most part, however, she did not even see the program. She saw, instead, herself, infinitely graceful, moving through the figures of the dance that had been so difficult for her to master.

The high-school folk-dancing class was made up of two kinds of performers—those with natural ability, who had themselves elected the class, and those who, in the language of the physical-education department, were "remedials." The remedials had been sent into the class willy-nilly in an effort to counteract in them defects ranging from antisocial attitudes to what Miss Ingols, the gym teacher, called "a general lack of grace." Cress had achieved the class under this final classification but now, at midterm, had so far outgrown it as to be the only remedial with a part in the festival.

The first five numbers on the program, "Tsiganotchka," "Ladies' Whim," "Meitschi Putz Di," "Hiawatha," and "Little Man in a Fix," Cress ignored. It was not only that she was not in these but that they were in no way as beautiful as "Road to the Isles," in which Mary Lou Hawkins, Chrystal O'Conor, Zelma Mayberry, Bernadine Deevers, and Crescent Delahanty took part. The mere sight of her name beside that of Bernadine Deevers, Tenant High School's most gifted dancer—most gifted *person*, really—instantly called up to Cress a vision of herself featly footing it in laced kirtle and starched skirts, a vision of herself dancing not only the outward steps of "Road to the Isles" but its inner meaning: what Miss Ingols had called "the achievement of the impossible."

Cress thought that she was particularly adapted to dancing that meaning because she had so recently come that way herself. If she had been given three wishes when school opened in September, two of them would have been that Bernadine be her friend and that she herself succeed in the folk-dancing class. Both had then seemed equally impossible. Now not only did she have a part in the festival but Bernadine was her dear friend and coming to spend the weekend with her. At the minute the evening reached what she considered its peak of mellowness, she intended to speak to her father and mother about the festival and Bernadine's visit. She was exceedingly uncertain about their performances on both these occasions.

The rain suddenly began to fall harder. Cress's father, hearing it on the roof, watched with gratification as the water streamed across the dark windowpanes. "Just what the oranges have been a-thirsting for," he said.

Mrs. Delahanty closed her book. "How's the schedule coming?" she asked her husband.

"O.K., I guess," said Mr. Delahanty.

Cress looked up from the festival program with embarrassment. The schedule was one of the things she wanted to speak to her father about. She hoped he wouldn't mention it while Bernadine was visiting them. Every winter, as work on the ranch slackened, he drew up a schedule for the better ordering of his life. And every spring, as work picked up, he abandoned it as easily as if it had never been. Last winter, he had made a plan called "A Schedule of Exercises to Ensure Absolute Fitness," which included not only the schedule of exercises and the hours at which he proposed to practice them but a list of the weaknesses they were to counteract. He had even gone so far, last winter, as to put on a pair of peculiar short pants and run six times around the orchard without stopping, arms flailing, chest pumping—a very embarrassing sight, and one that Cress could not possibly have explained to Bernadine.

This winter, the subject of her father's schedule-making was not in itself so unsuitable. He had bought a new encyclopedia set and was mapping out a reading program that would enable him, by a wise use of his spare time, to cover the entire field of human knowledge in a year. The name of the schedule, written at the top of a sheet of Cress's yellow graph paper, was, in fact, "Human Knowledge in a Year." There was nothing about this plan that would call for embarrassing public action, like running around the orchard in shorts, but it was so incredibly naïve and dreamy that Cress hoped her father would not speak of it. Bernadine was far too sophisticated for schedules.

"Where are you now on your schedule, John?" Mrs. Delahanty asked.

Mr. Delahanty, who liked to talk about his plans almost as much as he liked to make them, put down his pen and picked up the sheet of paper on which he had been writing. "I've got all the subjects I want to read up about listed, and the times I'll have free *for* reading listed. Nothing left to do now but decide what's the best time for what. For instance, if you were me, Gertrude, would you spend the fifteen minutes before breakfast on art? Or on archeology, say?"

"You don't ever have fifteen minutes before breakfast," Mrs. Delahanty said.

Mr. Delahanty picked up his pen. "I thought you wanted to discuss this."

"Oh, I do!" said Mrs. Delahanty. "Well if *I* had fifteen minutes before breakfast, *I'd* read about archeology."

"Why?" asked Mr. Delahanty.

"It's more orderly that way," Mrs. Delahanty said.

"Orderly?" asked Mr. Delahanty.

"A-r-c," Mrs. Delahanty spelled, "comes before a-r-t."

Mr. Delahanty made an impatient sound. "I'm not going at this alphabetically, Gertrude. Cut and dried. What I'm thinking about is what would make the most interesting morning reading. The most interesting and inspiring."

"Art is supposed to be more inspiring," Mrs. Delahanty told him. "If that's what you're after."

This seemed to decide Mr. Delahanty. "No, I think science should be the morning subject," he said, and wrote something at the top of a sheet—"Science," Cress supposed. "That's better," he said. "That leaves art for the evening, when I'll have time to read aloud to you."

"Don't change your schedule around for my sake, John," said Mrs. Delahanty, who hated being read to about anything.

"I'm not. All personal consideration aside, that's a more logical arrangement. Now the question is, which art?"

This seemed to Cress the moment for which she had been waiting. "Dancing is one of the earliest and most important of the arts," she said quickly.

"Oho!" said her father. "I thought you were in a coma."

"I've been rehearsing," said Cress.

"Rehearsing!" exclaimed Mr. Delahanty.

"In my mind," Cress said.

"So that's what was going on—'Ladies' Whim,' 'Tsiganotchka'—"

"Father," Cress interrupted, "I've told you and told you the t's silent. Why don't you take the program and practice the names? I'll help you." Cress got up and took the program across to her father.

"Practice them," said Mr. Delahanty with surprise, reading through the dances listed. "What do I care how they're pronounced? 'Korbushka,' 'Kohanotchka,'" he said, mispronouncing wildly. "I'm not going to Russia."

"But you're going to the folk-dance festival," Cress reminded him.

"I don't *have* to go. If you don't want—"

"I do, Father. You know I want you to go. Only I don't want you to mispronounce the names."

"Look, Cress," Mr. Delahanty said. "I promise you I'll keep my mouth shut the whole time I'm there. No one will know you have a father who can't pronounce. Mute I'll come and mute I'll go."

"I don't want you to be mute," Cress protested. "And even if I did, you couldn't very well be mute the whole time Bernadine's here. And Bernadine's the star of the program."

"To Bernadine," said Mr. Delahanty, referring to the program once again, "I shall speak of 'Badger,' and 'The Lumberman's Two Step.' I can pronounce them fine and they ought to hold Bernadine. She's not going to be here long, is she?"

"Friday to Monday," said Mrs. Delahanty.

"In that case," said Mr. Delahanty, "maybe I should find another one. How about 'The Irish Jollity,' Cress? Do I say that all right?"

"Now, John!" Mrs. Delahanty reproved her husband.

"It's all right for him to joke about it to me, Mother. But he mustn't before Bernadine. Bernadine's serious about dancing. She's going to be a great artist."

"A great dancer?" Mrs. Delahanty asked.

"She hasn't decided what kind of an artist yet," Cress said. "Only to be great in something."

"Well, well," said Mr. Delahanty. "I'm beginning to look forward to meeting Bernadine."

"You already have," Cress told him. "Bernadine was one of the girls who rode with us to the basketball game."

Mr. Delahanty squinted his eyes, as if trying to peer backward to the Friday two weeks before when he had provided Cress and four of her friends with transportation to an out-of-town game. He shook his head. "Can't recall any Bernadine," he said.

"She was the one in the front seat with us," Cress reminded him.

"That girl!" exclaimed Mr. Delahanty, remembering. "But her name wasn't Bernadine, was it?"

"No," Cress told him. "That's what I wanted to explain to you, because tomorrow's Friday, too."

Mr. Delahanty left desk and schedule and walked over in front of the fireplace. From this position, he could get a direct view of his daughter.

"What's this you're saying, Cress?" he asked. "Her name isn't Bernadine because tomorrow's Friday. Is that what you said?"

"Yes, it is," Cress told him, seriously. "Only it's not just tomorrow. Her name isn't Bernadine on any Friday."

Mr. Delahanty appealed to his wife. "Do you hear what I hear, Gertrude?"

"Mother," Cress protested, "this isn't anything funny. In fact, it's a complete tragedy."

"Well, Cress dear," her mother said reasonably, "I haven't said a word. And your father's just trying to get things straight."

"He's trying to be funny about a tragedy," Cress insisted obstinately.

"Now, Cress," Mr. Delahanty urged, "you're jumping to conclusions. Though I admit I think it's queer to have a name on Fridays you don't have the rest of the week. And I don't see anything tragic about it."

"That's what I'm trying to tell you, only you keep acting as if it's a joke."

"What is Bernadine's name on Fridays, Cress?" asked her mother.

"Nedra," said Cress solemnly.

Mr. Delahanty snapped his fingers. "Yes, sir," he said, "that's it! That's what they called her, all right."

"Of course," said Cress. "Everyone does on Fridays, out of respect for her sorrow."

"Just what *is* Bernadine's sorrow, Cress?" her mother asked.

"Bernadine never did say—out and out, that is. Once in a while she tries to. But she just can't. It overwhelms her. But we all know what, generally speaking, must have happened."

"What?" asked Mr. Delahanty. "Generally speaking?"

Cress looked at her father suspiciously, but his face was all sympathetic concern.

"On some Friday in the past," she said, "Nedra had to say no to someone. Someone she loved."

"How old is Berna—Nedra?" Mrs. Delahanty asked.

"Sixteen," Cress said. "Almost."

"Well, it couldn't have been too long ago then, could it?" her mother suggested.

"Was this person," Mr. Delahanty ventured, "this person Nedra said no to, a male?"

"Of course," said Cress. "I told you it was a complete tragedy, didn't I? His name was Ned. That much we know."

"Then the Nedra is in honor of—Ned?" asked her mother.

"In honor and loving memory," Cress told her. "On the very next Friday, Ned died."

Mr. Delahanty said nothing. Mrs. Delahanty said, "Poor boy!"

"I think he was probably more than a boy," Cress said. "He owned two drugstores."

After the elder Delahantys had thought about this for a while Mr. Delahanty asked, "This 'no' Bernadine—Nedra—said, was it to a proposal of marriage?"

"We don't ever ask about that," Cress told her father disapprovingly. "It doesn't seem like good taste to us."

"No, I don't suppose it is," Mr. Delahanty admitted.

"Anyway," Cress said, "that's Bernadine's tragedy and we all respect it and her wish to be called Nedra on Fridays. And tomorrow is a Friday, and it would be pretty awful to have her upset before the festival."

Mr. Delahanty stepped briskly back to his desk. "Don't you worry for a second, Cress," he said. "As far as I'm concerned, the girl's name is Nedra."

"Thank you, Father," Cress said. "I knew you'd understand. Now I'd better go to bed." At the door to the hallway, she turned and spoke once again. "If I were you, Father, I wouldn't say anything about your schedule to Bernadine."

"I hadn't planned on talking to her about it. But what's wrong with it?" Mr. Delahanty sounded a little testy.

"Oh, nothing," Cress assured him. "I think it's dear and sweet of you to make schedules. Only," she explained, "it's so idealistic."

After Cress left the room, Mr. Delahanty said, "What the hell's wrong with being idealistic?"

Cress thought that her friend, in her costume for "Fado Blanquita," the Spanish dance in which she performed the solo part, looked like the queen of grace and beauty. And she said so.

"This does rather suit my type," Bernadine admitted. She was leaning out from the opened casement window of Cress's room into the shimmering, rain-washed air. She tautened her costume's already tight bodice, fluffed up its already bouffant skirt, and extended her hands in one of the appealing gestures of the dance toward the trees of the orange orchard upon which the window opened.

"Is your father a shy man?" she asked.

Mr. Delahanty, who had been working near the driveway to the house when the two girls got off the school bus an hour before, had, instead of lingering to greet them, quickly disappeared behind a row of trees. Now, in rubber boots, carrying a light spade that he was using to test the depth to which the night before's rain had penetrated the soil, he came briefly into sight, waved his spade, and once again disappeared.

"No," said Cress, who thought her father rather bold, if anything. "He's just busy. After the rain, you know."

"Rain, sunshine. Sunshine, rain," Bernadine said understandingly. She moved her hands about in the placid afternoon air as if scooping up samples. "Farming is an awfully elemental life, I expect. My father"—Bernadine's father, J. M. Deevers, was vice-president of the Tenant First National Bank—"probably doesn't know one element from another. I expect your father's rather an elemental type, too, isn't he? Fundamentally, I mean?"

"I don't know, Nedra," Cress said humbly.

"He's black-haired," Bernadine said. "It's been my experience that black-haired men are very elemental." She brought her expressive hands slowly down to her curving red satin bodice. "You must have a good deal of confidence in your family to let them go tonight," she went on briskly.

"Let them!" Cress repeated, amazed at the word.

"Perhaps they're different from my family. Mine always keep me on pins and needles about what they're going to say and do next."

"Mine, too," Cress admitted, though loyalty to her father and mother would not permit her to say how greatly they worried her. She never went anyplace with them that she was not filled with a tremulous concern lest they do or say something that would discredit them all. She stayed with them. She attempted to guide them. She hearkened to every word said to them, so that she could prompt them with the right answers. But let them! "They always just take it for granted that where I go, they go," she said. "There's not much question of letting."

"Mine used to be that way," Bernadine confided. "But after what happened at the festival last year, I put my foot down. 'This year,' I told them, 'you're not going.'"

"What happened last year?" asked Cress, who had not then been a dancer.

"After the program was over last year, Miss Ingols asked for parent participation in the dancing. And my father participated. He danced the 'Hopak,' and pretty soon he was lifting Miss Ingols off the floor at every other jump."

"Oh, Nedra," Cress said. "How terrible! What did Ingols do?"

"Nothing," said Bernadine. "That was the disgusting part. As a matter of fact, she seemed to enjoy it. But you can imagine how I suffered."

Cress nodded. She could. She was thinking how she would suffer if her father, in addition to mispronouncing all the dances, went out on the gymnasium floor and, before all her friends, misdanced them.

"Are your parents the participating type?" Bernadine asked.

Cress nodded with sad conviction. "Father is. And Mother is if encouraged."

"You'd better warn them right away," Bernadine said. "Your father just came in the back door. You could warn him now."

Cress walked slowly down the hallway toward the kitchen. Before the evening was over, her father, too, would probably be jouncing Miss Ingols around, and even calling Bernadine Bernadine—then all would be ruined completely, all she had looked forward to for so long. In the kitchen, she noted signs of the special supper her mother was cooking because of Bernadine: the cole-slaw salad had shreds of green peppers and red apples mixed through it tonight to make it festive; the party sherbet glasses, with their long, icicle stems, awaited the lemon pudding. But her mother was out of the kitchen—on the back porch telling her father to hurry, because they would have to have dinner early if they were to get to the festival in time. "Festival!" Cress heard her father say. "I wish I'd never heard of that festival. How did Cress ever come to get mixed up in this dancing business, anyway?" he asked. "She's no dancer. Why, the poor kid can hardly get through a room without knocking something over. Let alone dance!"

"That's *why* she's mixed up with it," her mother explained. "To overcome her awkwardness. And she *is* better."

"But is she good enough?" asked her father. "I'd hate to think of her making a spectacle of herself—to say nothing of having to sit and watch it."

"Now, John," Cress heard her mother say soothingly. "You're always too concerned about Cress. Will she do this right? Will she do that right? Stop worrying. Cress'll probably be fine."

"Maybe fall on her ear, too," her father said morosely. "They oughtn't to put so much responsibility on kids. Performing in public. Doesn't it worry you any?"

"Certainly it worries me. But all parents worry. And remember, we'll have the star of the performance with us. You can concentrate on Nedra if watching Cress is too much for you."

"That Nedra! The only dance I can imagine that girl doing is one in which she would carry somebody's head on a platter."

Cress had started back down the hall before her father finished this sentence, but she had not gone so far as to miss its final word.

She stopped in the bathroom to have a drink of water and to see how she looked in the mirror over the washbasin. She looked different. For the first time in her life, she saw herself through other eyes than her own. Through her parents' eyes. Did parents worry about the figures their *children* cut? Were they embarrassed for *them*, and did they wonder if they were behaving suitably, stylishly, well? Cress felt a vacant, hollow space beneath her heart, which another glass of water did nothing to fill. Why, *I'm* all right, Cress thought. *I* know how to behave. I'll get by. *They're* the ones . . . but she looked at her face again and it was wavering, doubtful—not the triumphant face she had imagined, smiling in sureness as she danced the come-and-go figures of "Road to the Isles."

She went back to her room full of thought. Bernadine was changing her costume, and her muffled voice came from under all her skirts. "Did you tell them?" this muffled voice asked.

"No," said Cress, "I didn't."

"Why not? Won't you be worried?"

"They're the ones who are worrying. About me."

"About you?"

"Father thinks I may fall on my ear."

Bernadine, clear of her skirts, nodded in smiling agreement. "It's a possibility that sometimes occurs to *me*, Cress dear."

Cress gazed at her friend speculatively. "They're worried about you, too," she said.

"Me?" asked Bernadine, her smile fading.

"Father said the only dance he could imagine you doing was one with a head on a platter."

"Salome!" Bernadine exclaimed with pleasure. "Your father's imaginative, isn't he? Sympathetically imaginative?"

"I guess so," Cress said, and in her confusion told everything. "He keeps schedules."

"Schedules?"

"For the better ordering of his life."

Bernadine laughed again. "How precious!" she said.

Then, as if remembering after too long a lapse the day and her bereavement, she said, "Neddy was like that, too."

"Neddy," repeated Cress, pain for the present making Bernadine's past seem not only past but silly. "Oh, shut up about Neddy, *Bernadine!*"

Bernadine gave a little gasp. "Have you forgotten it's Friday?"

"I don't care what day it is," Cress said. She walked over to her bed, picked up the pillow, and lay down. Then she put the pillow over her face.

About the author

Jessamyn West (1907–   ) began writing stories when an attack of tuberculosis confined her to bed for a long period of time. She writes often of Indiana where she was born, and of California where she is now living. She knows the Quakers well, and her first book, *The Friendly Persuasion*, consisted of gently humorous sketches of a Quaker family living in Indiana at the time of the Civil War. She has written a number of stories about Cress Delahanty, portraying the often bewildering experiences of a high school girl with humor and understanding.

Questions for discussion

1. What discovery did Cress make about her parents and especially about her father? What did she learn about herself? About Bernadine?
2. In a sudden moment of insight near the end of the story, Cress changed a great deal. In what ways did she change?
3. Before Cress changed, she was patronizing to her parents. That is, out of her "superior" knowledge and experience she "graciously" consented to put up with them. What incidents in the story show this attitude?
4. How would you describe Mrs. Delahanty's attitude toward her husband?
5. What evidence is there that Mr. Delahanty realizes how and why Cress worries about him?
6. What is Bernadine's attitude toward Mr. Delahanty? Cite examples from the story.
7. What is the writer's attitude toward Cress in the early parts of the story? Does this attitude change to sympathy at the end? Give examples to show how the writer's attitude changes.
8. In many stories a character changes and is quite different at the end from what he was at the beginning. The writer must prepare the reader for a change such as this in order to make his story believable. The change in Cress's attitude toward her parents is a gradual one. At what point does it begin to change?
9. Of the three people in the Delahanty story, which one might have written the story in just the way it is written?

10. CHARACTER. A writer can portray a character *directly* by describing his appearance and telling what kind of a person he is. The writer may also portray a character *indirectly* through what the character says and does, and through what other people say about him. By what means is Mr. Delahanty's character portrayed? By what means do we learn about Cress?

Vocabulary growth

WORD FORMATION. In English, many words are made by adding prefixes and suffixes to base words. Thus, the words *act, inaction, active, inactive, activate* all grow out of the common base word, *act*. Find the base word from which each of the following is formed. Make at least one other word from the same base.

remedial	midterm	knowledge
infinitely	festival	reasonably
antisocial	unsuitable	idealistic
classification	enable	discredit

CONTEXT. On page 79, you read that Cress had a vision of herself "featly footing it in laced kirtle . . ." Reread the sentence and try to figure out a meaning for *featly*. Check your estimate with the dictionary On page 81, Mr. Delahanty says, "Mute I'll come and mute I'll go." Reread the passage and figure out a meaning for *mute*. Check your estimate with the dictionary.

For composition

1. Discuss in a rather light vein: "My Worries About My Parents"; "My Parents' Worries About Me."
2. Write a paragraph on "A Dream That I Made Come True."
3. If you were permitted to read Cress's diary, what would you find recorded there for Thursday night? For Friday night, the night after the dance festival?

Luke Baldwin's Vow

MORLEY CALLAGHAN

An orphan boy goes to live with his uncle and grows to love the uncle's old, half-blind dog. What can he do when the uncle decides that the dog is useless and must be put away?

THAT summer when twelve-year-old Luke Baldwin came to live with his Uncle Henry in the house on the stream by the sawmill, he did not forget that he had promised his dying father he would try to learn things from his uncle; so he used to watch him very carefully.

Uncle Henry, who was the manager of the sawmill, was a big, burly man weighing more than two hundred and thirty pounds, and he had a rough-skinned, brick-colored face. He looked like a powerful man, but his health was not good. He had aches and pains in his back and shoulders which puzzled the doctor. The first thing Luke learned about Uncle Henry was that everybody had great respect for him. The four men he employed in the sawmill were always polite and attentive when he spoke to them. His wife, Luke's Aunt Helen, a kindly, plump, straightforward woman, never argued with him. "You should try and be like your Uncle Henry," she would say to Luke. "He's so wonderfully practical. He takes care of everything in a sensible, easy way."

Luke used to trail around the sawmill after Uncle Henry not only because he liked the fresh clean smell of the newly cut wood and the big piles of sawdust, but because he was impressed by his uncle's precise, firm tone when he spoke to the men.

Sometimes Uncle Henry would stop and explain to Luke something about a piece of lumber. "Always try and learn the essential facts, son," he would say. "If you've got the facts, you know what's useful and what isn't useful, and no one can fool you."

He showed Luke that nothing of value was ever wasted around

90

the mill. Luke used to listen, and wonder if there was another man in the world who knew so well what was needed and what ought to be thrown away. Uncle Henry had known at once that Luke needed a bicycle to ride to his school, which was two miles away in town, and he bought him a good one. He knew that Luke needed good, serviceable clothes. He also knew exactly how much Aunt Helen needed to run the house, the price of everything, and how much a woman should be paid for doing the family washing. In the evenings Luke used to sit in the living room watching his uncle making notations in a black notebook which he always carried in his vest pocket, and he knew that he was assessing the value of the smallest transaction that had taken place during the day.

Luke promised himself that when he grew up he, too, would be admired for his good, sound judgment. But, of course, he couldn't always be watching and learning from his Uncle Henry, for too often when he watched him he thought of his own father; then he was lonely. So he began to build up another secret life for himself around the sawmill, and his companion was the eleven-year-old collie, Dan, a dog blind in one eye and with a slight limp in his left hind leg. Dan was a fat, slow-moving old dog. He was very affectionate and his eye was the color of amber. His fur was amber too. When Luke left for school in the morning, the old dog followed him for half a mile down the road, and when he returned in the afternoon, there was Dan waiting at the gate.

Sometimes they would play around the millpond or by the dam, or go down the stream to the lake. Luke was never lonely when the dog was with him. There was an old rowboat that they used as a pirate ship in the stream, and they would be pirates together, with Luke shouting instructions to Captain Dan and with the dog seeming to understand and wagging his tail enthusiastically. Its amber eye was alert, intelligent, and approving. Then they would plunge into the brush on the other side of the stream, pretending they were hunting tigers. Of course, the old dog was no longer much good for hunting; he was too slow and too lazy. Uncle Henry no longer used him for hunting rabbits or anything else.

When they came out of the brush, they would lie together on the cool, grassy bank being affectionate with each other, with Luke talking earnestly, while the collie, as Luke believed, smiled with the good eye. Lying in the grass, Luke would say things to Dan he could not say to his uncle or his aunt. Not that what he said was important; it was just stuff about himself that he might have told to his own father or mother if they had been alive. Then they would go back to the house for dinner, and after dinner Dan would follow him down the road to Mr. Kemp's house, where they would ask old Mr. Kemp if they could go with him to round up his four cows. The old man was always glad to see them. He seemed to like watching Luke and the collie running around the cows, pretending they were riding on a vast range in the foothills of the Rockies.

Uncle Henry no longer paid much attention to the collie, though once when he tripped over him on the veranda he shook his head and said thoughtfully, "Poor old fellow, he's through. Can't use him for anything. He just eats and sleeps and gets in the way."

One Sunday during Luke's summer holidays, when they had returned from church and had had their lunch, they had all moved out to the veranda where the collie was sleeping. Luke sat down on the steps, his back against the veranda post, Uncle Henry took the rocking chair, and Aunt Helen stretched herself out in the hammock, sighing contentedly. Then Luke, eyeing the collie, tapped the step with the palm of his hand, giving three little taps like a signal, and the old collie, lifting his head, got up stiffly with a slow wagging of the tail as an acknowledgment that the signal had been heard, and began to cross the veranda to Luke. But the dog was sleepy; his bad eye was turned to the rocking chair; in passing, his left front paw went under the rocker. With a frantic yelp, the dog went bounding down the steps and hobbled around the corner of the house, where he stopped, hearing Luke coming after him. All he needed was the touch of Luke's hand. Then he began to lick the hand methodically, as if apologizing.

"Luke," Uncle Henry called sharply, "bring that dog here."

When Luke led the collie back to the veranda, Uncle Henry nodded and said, "Thanks, Luke." Then he took out a cigar, lit it, put his big hands on his knees, and began to rock in the chair while he frowned and eyed the dog steadily. Obviously he was making some kind of an important decision about the collie.

"What's the matter, Uncle Henry?" Luke asked nervously.

"That dog can't see any more," Uncle Henry said.

"Oh, yes, he can," Luke said quickly. "His bad eye got turned to the chair, that's all, Uncle Henry."

"And his teeth are gone, too," Uncle Henry went on, paying no attention to what Luke had said. Turning to the hammock, he called, "Helen, sit up a minute, will you?"

When she got up and stood beside him, he went on, "I was thinking about this old dog the other day, Helen. It's not only that he's just about blind, but did you notice that when we drove up after church he didn't even bark?"

"It's a fact he didn't, Henry."

"No, not much good even as a watchdog now."

"Poor old fellow. It's a pity, isn't it?"

"And no good for hunting either. And he eats a lot, I suppose."

"About as much as he ever did, Henry."

"The plain fact is the old dog isn't worth his keep any more. It's time we got rid of him."

"It's always so hard to know how to get rid of a dog, Henry."

"I was thinking about it the other day. Some people think it's best to shoot a dog. I haven't had any shells for that shotgun for over a year. Poisoning is a hard death for a dog. Maybe drowning is the easiest and quickest way. Well, I'll speak to one of the mill hands and have him look after it."

Crouching on the ground, his arms around the old collie's neck, Luke cried out, "Uncle Henry, Dan's a wonderful dog! You don't know how wonderful he is!"

"He's just a very old dog, son," Uncle Henry said calmly. "The time comes when you have to get rid of any old dog. We've got to be practical about it. I'll get you a pup, son. A smart little dog that'll be worth its keep. A pup that will grow up with you."

"I don't want a pup!" Luke cried, turning his face away. Circling around him, the dog began to bark, then flick his long pink tongue at the back of Luke's neck.

Aunt Helen, catching her husband's eye, put her finger on her lips, warning him not to go on talking in front of the boy. "An old dog like that often wanders off into the brush and sort of picks a place to die when the time comes. Isn't that so, Henry?"

"Oh, sure," he agreed quickly. "In fact, when Dan didn't show up yesterday, I was sure that was what had happened." Then he yawned and seemed to forget about the dog.

But Luke was frightened, for he knew what his uncle was like. He knew that if his uncle had decided that the dog was useless and that it was sane and sensible to get rid of it, he would be ashamed of himself if he were diverted by any sentimental consideration. Luke knew in his heart that he couldn't move his uncle. All he could do, he thought, was keep the dog away from his uncle, keep him out of the house, feed him when Uncle Henry wasn't around.

Next day at noontime Luke saw his uncle walking from the mill toward the house with old Sam Carter, a mill hand. Sam Carter was a dull, stooped, slow-witted man of sixty with an iron-gray beard, who was wearing blue overalls and a blue shirt. He hardly ever spoke to anybody. Watching from the veranda, Luke noticed that his uncle suddenly gave Sam Carter a cigar, which Sam put in his pocket. Luke had never seen his uncle give Sam a cigar or pay much attention to him.

Then, after lunch, Uncle Henry said lazily that he would like Luke to take his bicycle and go into town and get him some cigars.

"I'll take Dan," Luke said.

"Better not, son," Uncle Henry said. "It'll take you all afternoon. I want those cigars. Get going, Luke."

His uncle's tone was so casual that Luke tried to believe they were not merely getting rid of him. Of course he had to do what he was told. He had never dared to refuse to obey an order from his uncle. But when he had taken his bicycle and had ridden down the path that followed the stream to the town road and had got about a quarter of a mile along the road, he found that all he could think of was his uncle handing old Sam Carter the cigar.

Slowing down, sick with worry now, he got off the bike and stood uncertainly on the sunlit road. Sam Carter was a gruff, aloof old man who would have no feeling for a dog. Then suddenly Luke could go no farther without getting some assurance that the collie would not be harmed while he was away. Across the fields he could see the house.

Leaving the bike in the ditch, he started to cross the field, intending to get close enough to the house so Dan could hear him if he whistled softly. He got about fifty yards away from the house and whistled and waited, but there was no sign of the dog, which might be asleep at the front of the house, he knew, or over at the sawmill. With the saws whining, the dog couldn't hear the soft whistle. For a few minutes Luke couldn't make up his mind what to do, then he decided to go back to the road, get on his bike, and go back the way he had come until he got to the place where the river path joined the road. There he could leave his bike, go up the path, then into the tall grass and get close to the front of the house and the sawmill without being seen.

He had followed the river path for about a hundred yards, and when he came to the place where the river began to bend sharply toward the house his heart fluttered and his legs felt paralyzed, for he saw the old rowboat in the one place where the river was deep, and in the rowboat was Sam Carter with the collie.

The bearded man in the blue overalls was smoking the cigar; the dog, with a rope around its neck, sat contentedly beside him, its tongue going out in a friendly lick at the hand holding the rope. It was all like a crazy dream picture to Luke; all wrong because it looked so lazy and friendly, even the curling smoke from Sam Carter's cigar. But as Luke cried out, "Dan! Dan! Come on, boy!" and the dog jumped at the water, he saw that Sam Carter's left hand was hanging deep in the water, holding a foot of rope with a heavy stone at the end. As Luke cried out wildly, "Don't! Please don't!" Carter dropped the stone, for the cry came too late; it was blurred by the screech of the big saws at the mill. But Carter was startled, and he stared stupidly at the riverbank, then he ducked his head and began to row quickly to the bank.

But Luke was watching the collie take what looked like a long, shallow dive, except that the hind legs suddenly kicked up above the surface, then shot down, and while he watched, Luke sobbed and trembled, for it was as if the happy secret part of his life around the sawmill was being torn away from him. But even while he watched, he seemed to be following a plan without knowing it, for he was already fumbling in his pocket for his jackknife, jerking the blade open, pulling off his pants, kicking his shoes off, while he muttered fiercely and prayed that Sam Carter would get out of sight.

It hardly took the mill hand a minute to reach the bank and go slinking furtively around the bend as if he felt that the boy was following him. But Luke hadn't taken his eyes off the exact spot in the water where Dan had disappeared. As soon as the mill hand was out of sight, Luke slid down the bank and took a leap at the water, the sun glistening on his slender body, his eyes wild with eagerness as he ran out to the deep place, then arched his back and dived, swimming under water, his open eyes getting used to the greenish-gray haze of the water, the sandy bottom, and the imbedded rocks.

His lungs began to ache, then he saw the shadow of the collie floating at the end of the taut rope, rock-held in the sand. He slashed at the rope with his knife. He couldn't get much strength in his arm because of the resistance of the water. He grabbed the rope with his left hand, hacking with his knife. The collie suddenly drifted up slowly, like a water-soaked log. Then his own head shot above the surface, and, while he was sucking in the air, he was drawing in the rope, pulling the collie toward him and treading water. In a few strokes he was away from the deep place and his feet touched the bottom.

Hoisting the collie out of the water, he scrambled toward the bank, lurching and stumbling in fright because the collie felt like a dead weight.

He went on up the bank and across the path to the tall grass, where he fell flat, hugging the dog and trying to warm him with his own body. But the collie didn't stir, the good amber eye remained closed. Then suddenly Luke wanted to act like a resourceful, competent man. Getting up on his knees, he stretched the dog out on its belly, drew him between his knees, felt with trembling hands for the soft places on the flanks just above the hipbones, and rocked back and forth, pressing with all his weight, then relaxing the pressure as he straightened up. He hoped that he was working the dog's lungs like a bellows. He had read that men who had been thought drowned had been saved in this way.

"Come on, Dan. Come on, old boy," he pleaded softly. As a little water came from the collie's mouth, Luke's heart jumped, and he muttered over and over, "You can't be dead, Dan! You can't, you can't! I won't let you die, Dan!" He rocked back and forth tirelessly, applying the pressure to the flanks. More water dribbled from the mouth. In the collie's body he felt a faint tremor. "Oh, gee, Dan, you're alive," he whispered. "Come on, boy. Keep it up."

With a cough the collie suddenly jerked his head back, the amber eye opened, and there they were looking at each other. Then the collie, thrusting his legs out stiffly, tried to hoist himself up, staggered, tried again, then stood there in a stupor. Then he shook himself like any other wet dog, turned his head, eyed Luke, and the red tongue came out in a weak flick at Luke's cheek.

"Lie down, Dan," Luke said. As the dog lay down beside him, Luke closed his eyes, buried his head in the wet fur, and wondered why all the muscles of his arms and legs began to jerk in a nervous reaction, now that it was all over. "Stay there, Dan," he said softly, and he went back to the path, got his clothes, and came back beside Dan and put them on. "I think we'd better get away from this spot, Dan," he said. "Keep down, boy. Come on." And he crawled on through the tall grass till they were about seventy-five yards from the place where he had undressed. There they lay down together.

In a little while he heard his aunt's voice calling, "Luke. Oh, Luke! Come here, Luke!"

"Quiet, Dan," Luke whispered. A few minutes passed, and then Uncle Henry called, "Luke, Luke!" and he began to come down the path. They could see him standing there, massive and imposing, his hands on his hips as he looked down the path; then he turned and went back to the house.

As he watched the sunlight shine on the back of his uncle's neck, the exultation Luke had felt at knowing the collie was safe beside him turned to bewildered despair, for he knew that even if he should be forgiven for saving the dog when he saw it drowning, the fact was that his uncle had been thwarted. His mind was made up to get rid of Dan, and in a few days' time, in another way, he would get rid of him, as he got rid of anything around the mill that he believed to be useless or a waste of money.

As he lay back and looked up at the hardly moving clouds, he began to grow frightened. He couldn't go back to the house, nor could he take the collie into the woods and hide him and feed him there unless he tied him up. If he didn't tie him up, Dan would wander back to the house.

"I guess there's just no place to go, Dan," he whispered sadly. "Even if we start off along the road, somebody is sure to see us."

But Dan was watching a butterfly that was circling crazily above them. Raising himself a little, Luke looked through the grass at the corner of the house, then he turned and looked the other way to the wide blue lake. With a sigh he lay down again, and for hours they lay there together, until there was no sound from the saws in the mill and the sun moved low in the western sky.

"Well, we can't stay here any longer, Dan," he said at last. "We'll just have to get as far away as we can. Keep down, old boy," and he began to crawl through the grass, going farther away from the house. When he could no longer be seen, he got up and began to trot across the field toward the gravel road leading to town.

On the road, the collie would turn from time to time as if wondering why Luke shuffled along, dragging his feet wearily, head down. "I'm stumped, that's all, Dan," Luke explained. "I can't seem to think of a place to take you."

When they were passing the Kemp place, they saw the old man sitting on the veranda, and Luke stopped. All he could think of was that Mr. Kemp had liked them both and it had been a pleasure to help him get the cows in the evening. Dan had always been with them. Staring at the figure of the old man on the veranda, he said in a worried tone, "I wish I could be sure of him, Dan. I wish he was a dumb, stupid man who wouldn't know or care whether you were worth anything. . . . Well, come on." He opened the gate bravely, but he felt shy and unimportant.

"Hello, son. What's on your mind?" Mr. Kemp called from the veranda. He was a thin, wiry man in a tan-colored shirt. He had a gray, untidy mustache, his skin was wrinkled and leathery, but his eyes were always friendly and amused.

"Could I speak to you, Mr. Kemp?" Luke asked when they were close to the veranda.

"Sure. Go ahead."

"It's about Dan. He's a great dog, but I guess you know that as well as I do. I was wondering if you could keep him here for me."

"Why should I keep Dan here, son?"

"Well, it's like this," Luke said, fumbling the words awkwardly. "My uncle won't let me keep him any more . . . says he's too old." His mouth began to tremble, then he blurted out the story.

"I see, I see," Mr. Kemp said slowly, and he got up and came over to the steps and sat down and began to stroke the collie's head. "Of course, Dan's an old dog, son," he said quietly. "And sooner or later you've got to get rid of an old dog. Your uncle knows that. Maybe it's true that Dan isn't worth his keep."

"He doesn't eat much, Mr. Kemp. Just one meal a day."

"I wouldn't want you to think your uncle was cruel and unfeeling, Luke," Mr. Kemp went on. "He's a fine man . . . maybe just a little bit too practical and straightforward."

"I guess that's right," Luke agreed, but he was really waiting and trusting the expression in the old man's eyes.

"Maybe you should make him a practical proposition."

"I—I don't know what you mean."

"Well, I sort of like the way you get the cows for me in the evenings," Mr. Kemp said, smiling to himself. "In fact, I don't think you need me to go along with you at all. Now, supposing I gave you seventy-five cents a week. Would you get the cows for me every night?"

"Sure I would, Mr. Kemp. I like doing it, anyway."

"All right, son. It's a deal. Now I'll tell you what to do. You go back to your uncle, and before he has a chance to open up on you, you say right out that you've come to him with a business proposition. Say it like a man, just like that. Offer to pay him the seventy-five cents a week for the dog's keep."

"But my uncle doesn't need seventy-five cents, Mr. Kemp," Luke said uneasily.

"Of course not," Mr. Kemp agreed. "It's the principle of the thing. Be confident. Remember that he's got nothing against the dog. Go to it, son. Let me know how you do," he added, with an amused smile. "If I know your uncle at all, I think it'll work."

"I'll try it, Mr. Kemp," Luke said. "Thanks very much." But he didn't have any confidence, for even though he knew that Mr. Kemp was a wise old man who would not deceive him, he couldn't believe that seventy-five cents a week would stop his uncle, who was an important man. "Come on, Dan," he called, and he went slowly and apprehensively back to the house.

When they were going up the path, his aunt cried from the open window, "Henry, Henry, in heaven's name, it's Luke with the dog!"

Ten paces from the veranda, Luke stopped and waited nervously for his uncle to come out. Uncle Henry came out in a rush, but when he saw the collie and Luke standing there, he stopped stiffly, turned pale, and his mouth hung open loosely.

"Luke," he whispered, "that dog had a stone around his neck."

"I fished him out of the stream," Luke said uneasily.

"Oh, oh, I see," Uncle Henry said, and gradually the color came back to his face. "You fished him out, eh?" he asked, still looking at the dog uneasily. "Well, you shouldn't have done that. I told Sam Carter to get rid of the dog, you know."

"Just a minute, Uncle Henry," Luke said, trying not to falter. He gained confidence as Aunt Helen came out and stood beside her husband, for her eyes seemed to be gentle, and he went on bravely, "I want to make you a practical proposition, Uncle Henry."

"A what?" Uncle Henry asked, still feeling insecure, and wishing the boy and the dog weren't confronting him.

"A practical proposition," Luke blurted out quickly. "I know Dan isn't worth his keep to you. I guess he isn't worth anything to anybody but me. So I'll pay you seventy-five cents a week for his keep."

"What's this?" Uncle Henry asked, looking bewildered. "Where would you get seventy-five cents a week, Luke?"

"I'm going to get the cows every night for Mr. Kemp."

"Oh, for heaven's sake, Henry," Aunt Helen pleaded, looking distressed, "let him keep the dog!" and she fled into the house.

"None of that kind of talk!" Uncle Henry called after her. "We've got to be sensible about this!" But he was shaken himself, and overwhelmed with a distress that destroyed all his confidence. As he sat down slowly in the rocking chair and stroked the side of his big face, he wanted to say weakly, "All right, keep the dog," but he was ashamed of being so weak and sentimental. He stubbornly refused to yield to this emotion; he was trying desperately to turn his emotion into a bit of good, useful common sense, so he could justify his distress. So he rocked and pondered. At last he smiled. "You're a smart little shaver, Luke," he said slowly. "Imagine you working it out like this. I'm tempted to accept your proposition."

"Gee, thanks, Uncle Henry."

"I'm accepting it because I think you'll learn something out of this," he went on ponderously.

"Yes, Uncle Henry."

"You'll learn that useless luxuries cost the smartest men hard-earned money."

"I don't mind."

"Well, it's a thing you'll have to learn sometime. I think you'll learn, too, because you certainly seem to have a practical streak in you. It's a streak I like to see in a boy. O.K., son," he said, and he smiled with relief and went into the house.

Turning to Dan, Luke whispered softly, "Well, what do you know about that?"

As he sat down on the step with the collie beside him and listened to Uncle Henry talking to his wife, he began to glow with exultation. Then gradually his exultation began to change to a vast wonder that Mr. Kemp should have had such a perfect understanding of Uncle Henry. He began to dream of someday being as wise as old Mr. Kemp and knowing exactly how to handle people. It was possible, too, that he had already learned some of the things about his uncle that his father had wanted him to learn.

Putting his head down on the dog's neck, he vowed to himself fervently that he would always have some money on hand, no matter what became of him, so that he would be able to protect all that was truly valuable from the practical people in the world.

About the author

Morley Callaghan (1903–   ) is one of the best known of Canadian writers. He was encouraged to follow a career of writing by Ernest Hemingway. Like Hemingway, Callaghan writes dialogue that is realistic and close to the speech of real people. He is best known in this country for his short stories. Callaghan graduated from the University of Toronto, and went on to become a lawyer, but he spends virtually all of his time at writing.

Questions for discussion

1. In what way was Luke's first impression of his uncle a favorable one?
2. At the beginning of the story Luke had vowed to learn all he could *from* Uncle Henry. By the end of the story he is learning *about* Uncle Henry. What is the difference? What was Luke learning about his uncle?
3. At the end of the story Luke wants to be as wise as Mr. Kemp. In what way? At the end, Luke makes a vow to himself. What is this vow?
4. Uncle Henry was upset when he saw Luke returning with the dog. Which of the following are the most likely reasons for his being upset. Find instances in the story to support your answers:
   a. He was angry at Luke and the dog.
   b. He was angry because his plan for getting rid of the dog had failed.
   c. He was ashamed because Luke had discovered what had happened.
   d. He was ashamed of having ordered the hired man to drown the dog.

    e. He was sad because he realized how much the dog meant to Luke.

5. Sam, the mill hand, accepted Uncle Henry's cigar, tied a rope around the dog's neck, and took him out on the lake. How did Sam feel about this job?

6. Uncle Henry's character is very carefully and clearly drawn in this story. The reader learns a great deal about him from the opinions of others: the sawmill workers and Aunt Helen, for example. Find the passages in which their opinions are given. What did Luke's father think of Uncle Henry? How did you know what Mr. Kemp thought of him?

7. Did Uncle Henry decide everything on a practical basis, or did he take the feelings of other people into account? Is he ever really touched by the human side of things? Cite evidence from the story.

8. Can you state the theme or central idea of the story? Read over the last page of the story for clues to the theme.

9. What are values? A value is something that you think is important. Some things are more important to you than others. So it may be said that everyone has a *scale* of values, running from the least to the most important. Your values help you to decide what to do in a new situation. What did Uncle Henry value the most? What did Luke value more highly?

10. In many situations a person must choose between one value and another. In such a case, there is a *conflict of values*. Luke had one value of loyalty and obedience to his uncle. What other value did this conflict with? Uncle Henry placed a high value on practicality. What value did this conflict with?

Vocabulary growth

WORD FORMATION. If you know how words are put together, you can often figure out the meaning of a new word that looks long and complicated. Certain noun suffixes are especially useful to know because they add little or no meaning to the word. Their function is to make a noun out of an adjective or verb. Among them are *-ness*, *-ance*, *-ation* (*-tion*, *-ion*), and *-ment*.

    a. The following words appear in "Luke Baldwin's Vow." Find the base word to which the noun suffix has been added.

notation	instruction	consideration
transaction	attention	assurance
judgment	exultation	eagerness

b. By adding one of the noun endings given above, make nouns out of the following verbs and adjectives. Check your spelling with the dictionary.

untidy	propose	busy
friendly	(to) state	weak
amuse	rid	appear
awkward	express	protect

For composition

1. Have you thought about your own scale of values? What are the most important things in your life? Here are some possibilities: *physical comfort, making a contribution to society, your family, your religious faith, popularity, being attached to the opposite sex.* You will think of others. Write a paper in which you state what is your highest value. You can show how much this value means to you by pointing out what things you would be willing to give up in order to live by this value.

2. Many humorous family stories often revolve about a pet. Do you remember when someone left the bird cage open and the parakeet escaped? Do you remember when the new puppy got up on the table and helped himself to the birthday cake? Write an account of a similar incident.

3. You may believe that people make too much of pets. If so, you will have instances and examples in mind. Write a paper on the subject, "Pets in Their Proper Place."

Molly Morgan

JOHN STEINBECK

As Molly Morgan sits through the ordeal of her first interview for her first job, her mind keeps recalling memories of the past. Through these flashbacks, the reader learns many things about her family that have an important bearing on the rest of the story. The story is realistic: there is happiness; there is sadness—and there is Molly Morgan.

MOLLY Morgan got off the train in Salinas and waited three quarters of an hour for the bus. The big automobile was empty except for the driver and Molly.

"I've never been to the Pastures of Heaven, you know," she said. "Is it far from the main road?"

"About three miles," said the driver.

"Will there be a car to take me into the valley?"

"No, not unless you're met."

"But how do people get in there?"

The driver ran over the flattened body of a jack rabbit with apparent satisfaction. "I only hit 'em when they're dead," he apologized. "In the dark, when they get caught in the lights, I try to miss 'em."

"Yes, but how am I going to get into the Pastures of Heaven?"

"I dunno. Walk, I guess. Most people walk if they ain't met."

When he set her down at the entrance to the dirt sideroad, Molly Morgan grimly picked up her suitcase and marched toward the draw in the hills. An old Ford truck squeaked up beside her.

"Goin' into the valley, ma'am?"

"Oh—yes, yes, I am."

"Well, get in, then. Needn't be scared. I'm Pat Humbert. I got a place in the Pastures."

Molly surveyed the grimy man and acknowledged his introduction. "I'm the new schoolteacher, I mean, I think I am. Do you know where Mr. Whiteside lives?"

"Sure, I go right by there. He's clerk of the board. I'm on the school board myself, you know. We wondered what you'd look like." Then he grew embarrassed at what he had said, and flushed under his coating of dirt. " 'Course I mean what you'd *be* like. Last teacher we had gave a good deal of trouble. She was all right, but she was sick —I mean, sick and nervous. Finally quit because she was sick."

Molly picked at the fingertips of her gloves. "My letter says I'm to call on Mr. Whiteside. Is he all right? I don't mean that. I mean— is he—what kind of a man is he?"

"Oh, you'll get along with him all right. He's a fine old man. Born in that house he lives in. Been to college, too. He's a good man. Been clerk of the board for over twenty years."

When he put her down in front of the big old house of John Whiteside, she was really frightened. "Now it's coming," she said to herself. "But there's nothing to be afraid of. He can't do anything to me." Molly was only nineteen. She felt that this moment of interview for her first job was a tremendous inch in her whole existence.

The walk up to the door did not reassure her, for the path lay between tight little flower beds hedged in with clipped box, seemingly planted with the admonition, "Now grow and multiply, but don't grow too high, nor multiply too greatly, and above all things, keep out of this path!" There was a hand on those flowers, a guiding and a correcting hand. The large white house was very dignified. Venetian blinds of yellow wood were tilted down to keep out the noon sun. Halfway up the path she came in sight of the entrance. There was a veranda as broad and warm and welcoming as an embrace. Through her mind flew the thought, "Surely you can tell the hospitality of a house by its entrance. Suppose it had a little door and no porch." But in spite of the welcoming of the wide steps and the big doorway, her timidities clung to her when she rang the bell. The big door opened, and a large, comfortable woman stood smiling at Molly.

"I hope you're not selling something," said Mrs. Whiteside. "I never want to buy anything and I always do, and then I'm mad."

Molly laughed. She felt suddenly very happy. Until that moment she hadn't known how frightened she really was. "Oh, no," she cried. "I'm the new schoolteacher. My letter says I'm to interview Mr. Whiteside. Can I see him?"

"Well, it's noon, and he's just finishing his dinner. Did you have dinner?"

"Oh, of course. I mean, no."

Mrs. Whiteside chuckled and stood aside for her to enter. "Well, I'm glad you're sure." She led Molly into a large dining room, lined with mahogany, glass-fronted dish closets. The square table was littered with the dishes of a meal. "Why, John must have finished and gone. Sit down, young woman. I'll bring back the roast."

"Oh, no. Really, thank you, no, I'll just talk to Mr. Whiteside and then go along."

"Sit down. You'll need nourishment to face John."

"Is—is he very stern, with new teachers, I mean?"

"Well," said Mrs. Whiteside. "That depends. If they haven't had their dinner, he's a regular bear. He shouts at them. But when they've just got up from the table, he's only just fierce."

Molly laughed happily. "You have children," she said. "Oh, you've raised lots of children—and you like them."

Mrs. Whiteside scowled. "One child raised me. Raised me right through the roof. It was too hard on me. He's out raising cows now, poor devils. I don't think I raised him very high."

When Molly had finished eating, Mrs. Whiteside threw open a side door and called, "John, here's someone to see you." She pushed Molly through the doorway into a room that was a kind of a library, for big bookcases were loaded with thick, old, comfortable books, all filigreed in gold. And it was a kind of a sitting room. There was a fireplace of brick with a mantel of little red tile bricks and the most extraordinary vases on the mantel. Hung on a nail over the mantel, slung really, like a rifle on a shoulder strap, was a huge meerschaum pipe in the Jaeger fashion. Big leather chairs with leather tassels hanging to them, stood about the fireplace, all of them patent rocking chairs with the kind of springs that chant when you rock them. And lastly, the room was a kind of an office, for there was an old-fashioned roll-top desk, and behind it sat John Whiteside. When he looked up, Molly saw that he had at once the kindest and the sternest eyes she had ever seen, and the whitest hair, too. Real blue-white, silky hair, a great duster of it.

"I am Mary Morgan," she began formally.

"Oh, yes, Miss Morgan, I've been expecting you. Won't you sit down?"

She sat in one of the big rockers, and the springs cried with sweet pain. "I love these chairs," she said. "We used to have one when I was a little girl." Then she felt silly. "I've come to interview you about this position. My letter said to do that."

"Don't be so tense, Miss Morgan. I've interviewed every teacher we've had for years. And," he said, smiling, "I still don't know how to go about it."

"Oh—I'm glad, Mr. Whiteside. I never asked for a job before. I was really afraid of it."

"Well, Miss Mary Morgan, as near as I can figure, the purpose of this interview is to give me a little knowledge of your past and of the kind of person you are. I'm supposed to know something about you when you've finished. And now that you know my purpose, I suppose you'll be self-conscious and anxious to give a good impression. Maybe if you just tell me a little about yourself, everything'll be all right. Just a few words about the kind of girl you are, and where you came from."

Molly nodded quickly. "Yes, I'll try to do that, Mr. Whiteside," and she dropped her mind back into the past.

There was the old, squalid, unpainted house with its wide back porch and the round washtubs leaning against the rail. High in the great willow tree her two brothers, Joe and Tom, crashed about crying, "Now I'm an eagle." "I'm a parrot." "Now I'm an old chicken." "Watch me!"

The screen door on the back porch opened, and their mother leaned tiredly out. Her hair would not lie smoothly no matter how much she combed it. Thick strings of it hung down beside her face. Her eyes were always a little red, and her hands and wrists painfully cracked. "Tom, Joe," she called. "You'll get hurt up there. Don't worry me so, boys! Don't you love your mother at all?" The voices in the tree were hushed. The shrieking spirits of the eagle and the old chicken were drenched in self-reproach. Molly sat in the dust, wrapping a rag around a stick and doing her best to imagine it a tall lady in a dress. "Molly, come in and stay with your mother. I'm so tired today."

Molly stood up the stick in the deep dust. "You, miss," she whispered fiercely. "You'll get whipped on your bare bottom when I come back." Then she obediently went into the house.

Her mother sat in a straight chair in the kitchen. "Draw up, Molly. Just sit with me for a little while. Love me, Molly! Love your mother a little bit. You are mother's good little girl, aren't you?" Molly squirmed on her chair. "Don't you love your mother, Molly?"

The little girl was very miserable. She knew her mother would cry in a moment, and then she would be compelled to stroke the stringy hair. Both she and her brothers knew they should love their mother. She did everything for them. They were ashamed that they hated to be near her, but they couldn't help it. When she called to them and they were not in sight, they pretended not to hear, and crept away, talking in whispers.

"Well, to begin with, we were very poor," Molly said to John Whiteside. "I guess we were really poverty-stricken. I had two brothers a little older than I. My father was a traveling salesman, but even so, my mother had to work. She worked terribly hard for us."

About once in every six months a great event occurred. In the morning the mother crept silently out of the bedroom. Her hair was brushed as smoothly as it could be; her eyes sparkled, and she looked happy and almost pretty. She whispered, "Quiet, children! Your father's home."

Molly and her brothers sneaked out of the house, but even in the yard they talked in excited whispers. The news traveled quickly about the neighborhood. Soon the yard was filled with whispering children. "They say their father's home." "Is your father really home?" "Where's he been this time?" By noon there were a dozen children in the yard, standing in expectant little groups, cautioning one another to be quiet.

About noon the screen door on the porch sprang open and whacked against the wall. Their father leaped out. "Hi," he yelled. "Hi, kids!" Molly and her brothers flung themselves upon him and hugged his legs, while he plucked them off and hurled them into the air like kittens.

Mrs. Morgan fluttered about, clucking with excitement, "Children, children. Don't muss your father's clothes."

The neighbor children threw handsprings and wrestled and shrieked with joy. It was better than any holiday.

"Wait till you see," their father cried. "Wait till you see what I brought you. It's a secret now." And when the hysteria had quieted a little he carried his suitcase out on the porch and opened it. There were presents such as no one had ever seen, mechanical toys unknown before—tin bugs that crawled, and astounding steam shovels that worked in sand. There were superb glass marbles with bears and dogs right in their centers. He had something for everyone, several things for everyone. It was all the great holidays packed into one.

Usually it was midafternoon before the children became calm enough not to shriek occasionally. But eventually George Morgan sat on the steps, and they all gathered about while he told his adventures. This time he had been to Mexico while there was a revolution. Again he had gone to Honolulu, had seen the volcano and had himself ridden on a surfboard. Always there were cities and people, strange people; always adventures and a hundred funny incidents, funnier than anything they had ever heard. It couldn't all be told at one time. After school they had to gather to hear more and more. Throughout the world George Morgan tramped, collecting glorious adventures.

"As far as my home life went," Miss Morgan said, "I guess I almost didn't have any father. He was able to get home very seldom from his business trips."

John Whiteside nodded gravely.

Molly's hands rustled in her lap and her eyes were dim.

One time he brought a dumpy, woolly puppy in a box, and it wet on the floor immediately.

"What kind of a dog is it?" Tom asked in his most sophisticated manner.

Their father laughed loudly. He was so young! He looked twenty years younger than their mother. "It's a dollar and a half dog," he explained. "You get an awful lot of kinds of dog for a dollar and a half. It's like this. . . . Suppose you go into a candy store and say, 'I want a nickel's worth of peppermints and gumdrops and licorice and raspberry chews.' Well, I went in and said, 'Give me a dollar and a half's worth of mixed dog.' That's the kind it is. It's Molly's dog, and she has to name it."

"I'm going to name it George," said Molly.

Her father bowed strangely to her, and said, "Thank you, Molly." They all noticed that he wasn't laughing at her, either.

Molly got up very early the next morning and took George about the yard to show him the secrets. She opened the hoard where two pennies and a gold policeman's button were buried. She hooked his little front paws over the back fence so he could look down the street at the schoolhouse. Lastly she climbed into the willow tree, carrying George under one arm. Tom came out of the house and sauntered under the tree. "Look out you don't drop him," Tom called, and just at that moment the puppy squirmed out of her arms and fell. He landed on the hard ground with a disgusting little thump. One leg bent out at a crazy angle, and the puppy screamed long, horrible screams, with sobs between breaths. Molly scrambled out of the tree, dull and stunned by the accident. Tom was standing over the puppy, his face white and twisted with pain, and George, the puppy, screamed on and on.

"We can't let him," Tom cried. "We can't let him." He ran to the woodpile and brought back a hatchet. Molly was too stupefied to look away, but Tom closed his eyes and struck. The screams stopped suddenly. Tom threw the hatchet from him and leaped over the back fence. Molly saw him running away as though he were being chased.

At that moment Joe and her father came out of the back door. Molly remembered how haggard and thin and gray her father's face was when he looked at the puppy. It was something in her father's face that started Molly to crying. "I dropped him out of the tree, and he hurt himself, and Tom hit him, and then Tom ran away." Her voice sounded sulky. Her father hugged Molly's head against his hip.

"Poor Tom!" he said. "Molly, you must remember never to say anything to Tom about it, and never to look at him as though you remembered." He threw a gunny sack over the puppy. "We must have a funeral," he said. "Did I ever tell you about the Chinese funeral I went to, about the colored paper they throw in the air, and the little fat roast pigs on the grave?" Joe edged in closer, and even Molly's eyes took on a gleam of interest. "Well, it was this way. . . ."

Molly looked up at John Whiteside and saw that he seemed to be studying a piece of paper on his desk. "When I was twelve years old, my father was killed in an accident," she said.

The great visits usually lasted about two weeks. Always there came an afternoon when George Morgan walked out into the town and did not come back until late at night. The mother made the children go to bed early, but they could hear him come home, stumbling a little against the furniture, and they could hear his voice through the wall. These were the only times when his voice was sad and discouraged. Lying with held breaths, in their beds, the children knew what that meant. In the morning he would be gone, and their hearts would be gone with him.

They had endless discussions about what he was doing. Their father was a glad argonaut, a silver knight. Virtue and Courage and Beauty—he wore a coat of them. "Sometime," the boys said, "sometime when we're big, we'll go with him and see all those things."

"I'll go, too," Molly insisted.

"Oh, you're a girl. You couldn't go, you know."

"But he'd let me go, you know he would. Sometime he'll take me with him. You see if he doesn't."

When he was gone their mother grew plaintive again, and her eyes reddened. Querulously she demanded their love, as though it were a package they could put in her hand.

One time their father went away, and he never came back. He had never sent any money, nor had he ever written to them, but this time he just disappeared for good. For two years they waited, and then their mother said he must be dead. The children shuddered at the thought, but they refused to believe it, because no one so beautiful and fine as their father could be dead. Some place in the world he was having adventures. There was some good reason why he couldn't come back to them. Some day when the reason was gone, he would come. Some morning he would be there with finer presents and better stories than ever before. But their mother said he must have had an accident. He must be dead. Their mother was distracted. She read those advertisements which offered to help her make money at home. The children made paper flowers and shamefacedly tried to sell them.

The boys tried to develop magazine routes, and the whole family nearly starved. Finally, when they couldn't stand it any longer, the boys ran away and joined the navy. After that Molly saw them as seldom as she had seen her father, and they were so changed, so hard and boisterous, that she didn't even care, for her brothers were strangers to her.

"I went through high school, and then I went to San Jose and entered Teachers' College. I worked for my board and room at the home of Mrs. Allen Morit. Before I finished school my mother died, so I guess I'm a kind of an orphan, you see."

"I'm sorry," John Whiteside murmured gently.

Molly flushed. "That wasn't a bid for sympathy, Mr. Whiteside. You said you wanted to know about me. Everyone has to be an orphan some time."

Molly worked for her board and room. She did the work of a full time servant, only she received no pay. Money for clothes had to be accumulated by working in a store during summer vacation. Mrs. Morit trained her girls. "I can take a green girl, not worth a cent," she often said, "and when that girl's worked for me six months, she can get fifty dollars a month. Lots of women know it, and they just snap up my girls. This is the first schoolgirl I've tried, but even she shows a lot of improvement. She reads too much though. I always say a servant should be asleep by ten o'clock, or else she can't do her work right."

Mrs. Morit's method was one of constant criticism and nagging, carried on in a just, firm tone. "Now, Molly, I don't want to find fault, but if you don't wipe the silver drier than that, it'll have streaks."—"The butter knife goes this way, Molly. Then you can put the tumbler here."

"I always give a reason for everything," she told her friends.

In the evening, after the dishes were washed, Molly sat on her bed and studied, and when the light was off, she lay on her bed and thought of her father. It was ridiculous to do it, she knew. It was a waste of time. Her father came up to the door, wearing a cutaway coat, and striped trousers and a top hat. He carried a huge bouquet of red roses in his hand. "I couldn't come before, Molly. Get on your coat quickly. First we're going down to get that evening dress in the window of Prussia's, but we'll have to hurry. I have tickets for the train to New York tonight. Hurry up, Molly! Don't stand there gawping." It was silly. Her father was dead. No, she didn't really believe he was dead. Somewhere in the world he lived beautifully, and sometime he would come back.

Molly told one of her friends at school, "I don't really believe it, you see, but I don't disbelieve it. If I ever knew he was dead, why it would be awful. I don't know what I'd do then. I don't want to think about *knowing* he's dead."

When her mother died, she felt little besides shame. Her mother had wanted so much to be loved, and she hadn't known how to draw love. Her importunities had bothered the children and driven them away.

"Well, that's about all," Molly finished. "I got my diploma, and then I was sent down here."

"It was about the easiest interview I ever had," John Whiteside said.

"Do you think I'll get the position, then?"

The old man gave a quick, twinkly glance at the big meerschaum hanging over the mantel.

"That's his friend," Molly thought. "He has secrets with that pipe."

"Yes, I think you'll get the job. I think you have it already. Now, Miss Morgan, where are you going to live? You must find board and room some place."

Before she knew she was going to say it, she had blurted, "I want to live here."

John Whiteside opened his eyes in astonishment. "But we never take boarders, Miss Morgan."

"Oh, I'm sorry I said that. I just like it so much here, you see."

He called, "Willa," and when his wife stood in the half-open door, "This young lady wants to board with us. She's the new teacher."

Mrs. Whiteside frowned. "Couldn't think of it. We never take boarders. She's too pretty to be around that fool of a Bill. What would happen to those cows of his? It'd be a lot of trouble. You can sleep in the third bedroom upstairs," she said to Molly. "It doesn't catch much sun anyway."

Life changed its face. All of a sudden Molly found she was a queen. From the first day the children of the school adored her, for she understood them, and what was more, she let them understand her. It took her some time to realize that she had become an important person. If two men got to arguing at the store about a point of history or literature or mathematics, and the argument deadlocked, it ended up, "Take it to the teacher! If she doesn't know, she'll find it." Molly was very proud to be able to decide such questions. At parties she had to help with the decorations and to plan refreshments.

"I think we'll put pine boughs around everywhere. They're pretty, and they smell so good. They smell like a party." She was supposed to know everything and to help with everything, and she loved it.

At the Whiteside home she slaved in the kitchen under the mutterings of Willa. At the end of six months, Mrs. Whiteside grumbled to her husband, "Now if Bill only had any sense. But then," she continued, "if *she* has any sense—" and there she left it.

At night Molly wrote letters to the few friends she had made in Teachers' College, letters full of little stories about her neighbors, and full of joy. She must attend every party because of the social prestige of her position. On Saturdays she ran about the hills and brought back ferns and wild flowers to plant about the house.

Bill Whiteside took one look at Molly and scuttled back to his cows. It was a long time before he found the courage to talk to her very much. He was a big, simple young man who had neither his father's balance nor his mother's humor. Eventually, however, he trailed after Molly and looked after her from distances.

One evening, with a kind of feeling of thanksgiving for her happiness, Molly told Bill about her father. They were sitting in canvas chairs on the wide veranda, waiting for the moon. She told him about the visits, and then about the disappearance. "Do you see what I have, Bill?" she cried. "My lovely father is some place. He's mine. You think he's living, don't you, Bill?"

"Might be," said Bill. "From what you say, he was a kind of an irresponsible cuss, though. Excuse me, Molly. Still, if he's alive, it's funny he never wrote."

Molly felt cold. It was just the kind of reasoning she had successfully avoided for so long. "Of course," she said stiffly, "I know that. I have to do some work now, Bill."

High up on a hill that edged the valley of the Pastures of Heaven, there was an old cabin which commanded a view of the whole country and of all the roads in the vicinity. It was said that the bandit Vasquez had built the cabin and lived in it for a year while the posses went crashing through the country looking for him. It was a landmark. All the people of the valley had been to see it at one time or another. Nearly everyone asked Molly whether she had been there yet. "No," she said, "but I will go up some day. I'll go some Saturday. I know where the trail to it is." One morning she dressed in her new hiking boots and corduroy skirt. Bill sidled up and offered to accompany her. "No," she said. "You have work to do. I can't take you away from it."

"Work be hanged!" said Bill.

"Well, I'd rather go alone. I don't want to hurt your feelings, but I just want to go alone, Bill." She was sorry not to let him accompany her, but his remark about her father had frightened her. "I want to have an adventure," she said to herself. "If Bill comes along, it won't be an adventure at all. It'll just be a trip." It took her an hour and a half to climb up the steep trail under the oaks. The leaves on the ground were as slippery as glass, and the sun was hot. The good smell of ferns and dank moss and yerba buena filled the air. When Molly came at last to the ridge crest, she was damp and winded. The cabin stood in a small clearing in the brush, a little square wooden room with no windows. Its doorless entrance was a black shadow. The place was quiet, the kind of humming quiet that flies and bees and crickets make. The whole hillside sang softly in the sun. Molly approached on tiptoe. Her heart was beating violently.

"Now I'm having an adventure," she whispered. "Now I'm right in the middle of an adventure at Vasquez' cabin. She peered in at the doorway and saw a lizard scuttle out of sight. A cobweb fell across her forehead and seemed to try to restrain her. There was nothing at all in the cabin, nothing but the dirt floor and the rotting wooden walls, and the dry, deserted smell of the earth that has long been covered from the sun. Molly was filled with excitement. "At night he sat in there. Sometimes when he heard noises like men creeping up on him, he went out of the door like the ghost of a shadow, and just melted into the darkness." She looked down on the valley of the Pastures of Heaven. The orchards lay in dark green squares; the grain was yellow, and the hills behind, a light brown washed with lavender. Among the farms the roads twisted and curled, avoiding a field, looping around a huge tree, half circling a hill flank. Over the whole valley was stretched a veil of heat shimmer. "Unreal," Molly whispered, "fantastic. It's a story, a real story, and I'm having an adventure." A breeze rose out of the valley like the sigh of a sleeper, and then subsided.

"In the daytime that young Vasquez looked down on the valley just as I'm looking. He stood right here, and looked at the roads down there. He wore a purple vest braided with gold, and the trousers on his slim legs widened at the bottom like the mouths of trumpets. His spur rowels were wrapped with silk ribbons to keep them from clinking. Sometimes he saw the posses riding by on the road below. Lucky for him the men bent over their horses' necks, and didn't look up at the hilltops. Vasquez laughed, but he was afraid, too. Sometimes he sang. His songs were soft and sad because he knew he couldn't live very long."

Molly sat down on the slope and rested her chin in her cupped hands. Young Vasquez was standing beside her, and Vasquez had her father's gay face, his shining eyes as he came on the porch shouting, "Hi, Kids!" This was the kind of adventure her father had. Molly shook herself and stood up. "Now I want to go back to the first and think it all over again."

In the late afternoon Mrs. Whiteside sent Bill out to look for Molly. "She might have turned an ankle, you know." But Molly emerged from the trail just as Bill approached it from the road.

"We were beginning to wonder if you'd got lost," he said. "Did you go up to the cabin?"

"Yes."

"Funny old box, isn't it? Just an old woodshed. There are a dozen just like it down here. You'd be surprised, though, how many people go up there to look at it. The funny part is, nobody's sure Vasquez was ever there."

"Oh, I think he must have been there."

"What makes you think that?"

"I don't know."

Bill became serious. "Everybody thinks Vasquez was a kind of a hero, when really he was just a thief. He started in stealing sheep and horses and ended up robbing stages. He had to kill a few people to do it. It seems to me, Molly, we ought to teach people to hate robbers, not worship them."

"Of course, Bill," she said wearily. "You're perfectly right. Would you mind not talking for a little while, Bill? I guess I'm a little tired, and nervous, too."

The year wheeled around. Pussywillows had their kittens, and wild flowers covered the hills. Molly found herself wanted and needed in the valley. She even attended school board meetings. There had been a time when those secret and august conferences were held behind closed doors, a mystery and a terror to everyone. Now that Molly was asked to step into John Whiteside's sitting room, she found that the board discussed crops, told stories, and circulated mild gossip.

Bert Munroe had been elected early in the fall, and by the spring-time he was the most energetic member. He it was who planned dances at the schoolhouse, who insisted upon having plays and picnics. He even offered prizes for the best report cards in the school. The board was coming to rely pretty much on Bert Munroe.

One evening Molly came down late from her room. As always, when the board was meeting, Mrs. Whiteside sat in the dining room. "I don't think I'll go in to the meeting," Molly said. "Let them have one time to themselves. Sometimes I feel that they would tell other kinds of stories if I weren't there."

"You go on in, Molly! They can't hold a board meeting without you. They're so used to you, they'd be lost. Besides. I'm not at all sure I want them to tell those other stories."

Obediently Molly knocked on the door and went into the sitting room. Bert Munroe paused politely in the story he was narrating. "I was just telling about my new farm hand, Miss Morgan. I'll start over again, 'cause it's kind of funny. You see, I needed a hay hand, and I picked this fellow up under the Salinas River bridge. He was pretty drunk, but he wanted a job. Now I've got him, I find he isn't worth a cent as a hand, but I can't get rid of him. That son of a gun has been every place. You ought to hear him tell about the places he's been. My kids wouldn't let me get rid of him if I wanted to. Why he can take the littlest thing he's seen and make a fine story out of it. My kids just sit around with their ears spread, listening to him. Well, about twice a month he walks into Salinas and goes on a bust. He's one of those dirty, periodic drunks. The Salinas cops always call me up when they find him in a gutter, and I have to drive in to get him. And you know, when he comes out of it, he's always got some kind of present in his pocket for my kid Manny. There's nothing you can do with a man like that. He disarms you. I don't get a dollar's worth of work a month out of him."

Molly felt a sick dread rising in her. The men were laughing at the story. "You're too soft, Bert. You can't afford to keep an enter-tainer on the place. I'd sure get rid of him quick."

Molly stood up. She was dreadfully afraid someone would ask the man's name. "I'm not feeling very well tonight," she said. "If you gentlemen will excuse me, I think I'll go to bed." The men stood up while she left the room. In her bed she buried her head in the pillow. "It's crazy," she said to herself. "There isn't a chance in the world. I'm forgetting all about it right now." But she found to her dismay that she was crying.

The next few weeks were agonizing to Molly. She was reluctant to leave the house. Walking to and from school she watched the road ahead of her. "If I see any kind of a stranger I'll run away. But that's foolish. I'm being a fool." Only in her own room did she feel safe. Her terror was making her lose color, was taking the glint out of her eyes.

"Molly, you ought to go to bed," Mrs. Whiteside insisted. "Don't be a little idiot. Do I have to smack you the way I do Bill to make you go to bed?" But Molly would not go to bed. She thought too many things when she was in bed.

The next time the board met, Bert Munroe did not appear. Molly felt reassured and almost happy at his absence.

"You're feeling better, aren't you, Miss Morgan?"

"Oh, yes. It was only a little thing, a kind of a cold. If I'd gone to bed I might have been really sick."

The meeting was an hour gone before Bert Munroe came in. "Sorry to be late," he apologized. "The same old thing happened. My so-called hay hand was asleep in the street in Salinas. What a mess! He's out in the car sleeping it off now. I'll have to hose the car out tomorrow."

Molly's throat closed with terror. For a second she thought she was going to faint. "Excuse me, I must go," she cried, and ran out of the room. She walked into the dark hallway and steadied herself against the wall. Then slowly and automatically she marched out of the front door and down the steps. The night was filled with whispers. Out in the road she could see the black mass that was Bert Munroe's car. She was surprised at the way her footsteps plodded down the path of their own volition. "Now I'm killing myself," she said. "Now I'm throwing everything away. I wonder why." The gate was under her hand, and her hand flexed to open it. Then a tiny breeze sprang up and brought to her nose the sharp foulness of vomit. She heard a blubbering, drunken snore. Instantly something whirled in her head. Molly spun around and ran frantically back to the house. In her room she locked the door and sat stiffly down, panting with the effort of her run. It seemed hours before she heard the men go out of the house, calling their good-nights. Then Bert's motor started, and the sound of it died away down the road. Now that she was ready to go she felt paralyzed.

John Whiteside was writing at his desk when Molly entered the sitting room. He looked up questioningly at her. "You aren't well, Miss Morgan. You need a doctor."

She planted herself woodenly beside the desk. "Could you get a substitute teacher for me?" she asked.

"Of course I could. You pile right into bed and I'll call a doctor."

"It isn't that, Mr. Whiteside. I want to go away tonight."

"What are you talking about? You aren't well."

"I told you my father was dead. I don't know whether he's dead or not. I'm afraid—I want to go away tonight."

He stared intently at her. "Tell me what you mean," he said softly.

"If I should see that drunken man of Mr. Munroe's—" she paused, suddenly terrified at what she was about to say.

John Whiteside nodded very slowly.

"No," she cried. "I don't think that. I'm sure I don't."

"I'd like to do something, Molly."

"I don't want to go, I love it here—But I'm afraid. It's so important to me."

John Whiteside stood up and came close to her and put his arm about her shoulders. "I don't think I understand, quite," he said. "I don't think I want to understand. That isn't necessary." He seemed to be talking to himself. "It wouldn't be quite courteous—to understand."

"Once I'm away I'll be able not to believe it," Molly whimpered.

He gave her shoulders one quick squeeze with his encircling arm. "You run upstairs and pack your things, Molly," he said. "I'll get out the car and drive you right in to Salinas now."

About the author

John Steinbeck (1902–   ) places many of his stories in the setting of California, where he was born. During the depression of the 1930's he earned his living at a variety of odd jobs. Packing fruit, carrying a hod, working as a painter, and a reporter, Steinbeck gathered impressions and insights into people that were later to appear throughout his stories and novels. *The Grapes of Wrath*, dealing with migratory workers and their pitiful struggle for survival in the depression years, won for him the Pulitzer Prize. Many of his emotion-packed stories have been turned into highly successful films and plays.

Questions for discussion

1. Can you justify Molly's decision to run away? Was it a responsible thing to do? Was it realistic? Why did she decide to go? Molly rejected her father. Did she also condemn him?
2. Study the Vocabulary Growth section first. It will help you answer these questions:
    a. Did the Morgan children have *illusions* about their father? Did they have *illusions* about their mother? Explain.
    b. Did the father try to *delude* his children? Did he really enjoy his children? Cite evidence from the story.
    c. Did the father *elude* his responsibilities to his family? Support your answer with evidence from the story.
    d. At what point did *disillusionment* come to Molly?
3. Why was Molly so attracted to Mr. and Mrs. Whiteside? What did they provide for her that she had missed before?
4. Compassion is the quality of real and sympathetic feeling for another person who is in trouble. Is there an example of compassion in this story? Support your view with evidence from the story.
5. Do you think that the account of Vasquez belongs in the story? To what other character in the story is Vasquez similar? What is Molly's feeling about Vasquez? Why do you think the author put the account of Vasquez into the story?
6. Daydreaming may be good or bad, depending upon the reasons why a person indulges in it. Daydreams may be a stimulus to make one work hard and effectively. They may also be an escape from reality which prevents a person from doing what he should. What effect had daydreaming on Molly?
7. How did you feel about the unhappy ending of this story? Was it reasonable in terms of what we know about Molly and about Mr. Whiteside? Does a story have to have a happy ending in order to be satisfying? Show how a happy ending would have spoiled this story?
8. By what means does the author portray Molly's mother and father? Does he portray them *directly* by telling about them? Does he portray them *indirectly* by showing how other people react to them? By what the mother and father say and do? Give examples.
9. By what means does the author portray Molly? Give examples. Like most people, Molly was a mixture of strength and weakness, of

romantic and realist. Give examples that illustrate both sides of her character.

10. *Pathos* describes a situation in which someone suffers hardships or pain which he has done nothing to deserve. Or it may describe a situation in which a person suffers out of all proportion to his mistake, or fault, or guilt. *Tragedy* describes a situation in which a person suffers death, disaster, or defeat, because he cannot surmount the difficulties that face him.

    a. Is there a character in this story to whom the word *tragic* properly applies? Explain your choice.

    b. Is there a character in the story to whom the word *pathetic* properly applies? Explain your choice.

Vocabulary growth

For many centuries, Latin was the language that educated people used in reading and writing. Many of our words are built upon Latin roots. The word *ludicrous*, for example, is based upon a Latin word meaning "to play." You can find the root *-lud-* in many words:

    a. *delusion, delude*—To *delude* is to deceive.

    b. *elusion, elude*—To *elude* is to avoid slyly, to escape from.

    c. *allusion, allude*—To *allude* to something means to refer to it, to point it out.

    d. *illusion* (the verb is not often used). An *illusion* is a deceptive image or deceptive vision. A mirage in the desert is an illusion.

    e. *disillusion*, or *disillusionment*—To *disillusion* is to free from a deception.

For composition

1. What did Molly write in her diary that night when she was alone in Salinas? Pretend that you are Molly on that night. Make an entry in your diary, describing what you have seen and felt in the course of the day, and what you are feeling this night.

2. Have you ever been disillusioned with someone important in your life? Write a paragraph showing how you felt at the awful moment of discovery.

3. Have you ever had an important interview for a job, or for any other reason? Write a paragraph describing your feelings at the time.

4. Molly found herself in a number of situations in which she might have acted with *heroism*, or with *cowardice*. Write a brief paper in which you attempt to show clearly the difference between these two words.

Water Never Hurt a Man

WALTER D. EDMONDS

Today, if the son of a lawyer, or the son of an electrician wishes to follow in his father's footsteps, he goes to school for training. In the early years of our country, a boy could learn a profession or trade by working alongside his father.

Life on the Erie Canal in the 1830's was rugged, adventurous and exciting. Towboats were pulled forward by horses that trod a towpath which ran along the edge of the canal. They moved thousands of tons of manufactured goods westward to the settlers, and towed thousands of tons of farm goods back to the East.

Young John Brace, in his eagerness to be a part of all this wonder of the canal, could not know in advance the great price to be paid in hard work. What he did know was that he had often seen his father standing proudly in the bow of the *Bacconola*, directing the towboat safely through the heavy traffic. John's heart must have leaped when one day his father finally said, "John's old enough to be a driver boy, he's coming along with me."

HE trudged with his hands tight fists in his pockets, his head bowed to the wind and rain. Ahead of him in the darkness, so that he could hear the squdge of their hoofs, the towing team bowed their necks against the collars. He could not see them in the darkness. When he lifted his face the rain cut at his eyes; and when lightning split the darkness he shut his eyes tight and pulled his head closer into his coat collar, waiting blindly for the thunder. Once in a lull he looked back. He could barely make out the bow lantern and the arrows of gray rain slanting against it. Between him and the light he caught glimpses of the tow rope, dipped slightly between the team's heaves, and the roughened water in the canal. Somewhere back of the light his father stood by the rudder-sweep, his beard curled and wet, his eyes slits, sighting for the bank. John wanted to go back, wanted to tie-by for the night, wanted to be in the bunk with his head buried in the friendly, musty smell of the blanket, where the storm could not reach him. He had gone back once, but his father had reached for his belt, saying, "Go on back. Watter never hurt a man. It keeps his hide from cracking."

John had gone back to the team. They did not need his guidance. But it was his place to keep the rope from fouling if a packet boat coming their way signaled to pass. He was afraid of his father at night, afraid of the big belt and strong hands with hair on the fingers over the knuckles. He caught up with the plodding horses and let the rain have its way. At each stroke of lightning his small back stiffened. It was his first year on the canal and he was afraid of storms at night.

He had been proud that spring when his father said, "John's old enough to be a driver boy, he's coming along with me and the *Bacconola.*" He had showed his dollar to his brothers and sisters, first pay in advance, and his father had bought him a pair of cowhide boots from the cobbler when he came to the village. Later, when the frost was out of the mud, John would go barefoot.

He was proud of his father. In Westernville, with other small boys, he had heard the dock loafers talking about his father, George Brace, bully of the Black River Canal. In some strange way they had news of every fight his father fought a day after it happened. "George licked the Amsterdam Bully Wednesday mornin'. Lock fifty-nine. It tuk nineteen minits only." "George is a great hand. Them big ditch bezabors is learning about George." A stranger had said, "Wait till Buffalo Joe meets up with him." There was silence then. Buffalo Joe Buller, he was bully of the western end of the Erie. A pea-souper, a Canadian, he fought the Erie bullies down one by one, and when he licked them he marked them with his boot in the Canadian style. It had a cross of nails to mark the beaten man's face. "You wait," said the stranger.

Little John, listening then, felt shivers down his back. But now, with the wind and rain, and the lightning tumbling the clouds apart, he forgot. They were on the long haul westward, to Buffalo, with plows aboard, full drafted in Rome. They had had to leave three hundred weight on the dock.

He felt his muddy boots slip in the towpath. He heard the squelching of the horses. Squelch-squelch, a steady rhythm as they kept step.

Once the lightning caught his eyes; and he had a clear view of trees beyond the canal-side meadow, their budded twigs bent down, like old women with their backs to the storm, and the flat, sharp wall of a canal house, sixty yards behind him. He had not even seen it as he passed. The rain was finding a channel down his neck. It crept farther, bit by bit, with a cold touch. He could feel his fists white in his pockets from clenching them. His legs ached with the slippery going. They had had supper at six, tied up by the bank, and John had eaten his plate of beans. He had felt sleepy afterward, barely noticing his father's big body bent over the dishpan. It was warm in the cabin, with the little stove roaring red hot, and his small hat hanging beside his father's cap on the door.

He had been almost asleep when his father's hand shook him roughly, then tumbled him from his chair. "Get out, John. Them plows we've got has to get west for spring plowing. We'll pick up Bob in Syracuse, then we'll have a better chance to rest. Get out now," and he had reached for his belt.

What did John care for the old plows anyway? But it hadn't then begun to storm, and he had gone, with a tired sense of importance. One had to keep freight moving on the old Erie. The old *Bacconola* always made fast hauls. He had been proud and shouted in a high voice to the tired horses and kicked one with his new boots.

But now he did not care about the plows. He wished the crazy old *Bacconola* would spring a leak in her flat bottom, so they would have to stop till the hurry-up boat came along and patched her up. He thought of her now, bitterly, with her scabs of orange paint. "Crummy old blister," he called her to himself and made names to himself, which he said aloud to the horses in a shrill voice. He was only twelve, with all the bitterness of twelve, and the world was a hateful thing.

A water rat went off the towpath with a splash, and a frog squeaked.

He glanced up to see a team on the opposite towpath heading east. "Hey, there!" yelled the driver in a hoarse voice; but John was too tired to answer. He liked to yell back in the daytime and crack his whip. But he had dropped his whip a while back. He would get a licking for that in the morning. But he didn't care. To hell with the whip and the driver and Pa.

"Hey, there!" shouted the other driver, a voice in the rain. "All right, all right, you dirty pup. Eat rain, if you want to and go drownd."

The rain took the voice, and the boat came by, silently, noiseless as oil, with its bow light a yellow torch against the rain. The steersman gave a toot upon the horn, but the sound bubbled through the water in it, and the steersman swore.

They were still on the long level, alone once more. It must be midnight. If only the lock would show. In Syracuse, Bob would come. He took turns driving and steering and cooking—a little man with a bent shoulder who had dizzy spells once in a while.

At the lock John could sit down and rest and listen to the tender snarling at his sluices while the boat went down, and heaving at his gate beam, while John's father heaved against the other. He was crazy, the lock-keeper was; all lock-keepers were crazy. John's father always said so. John had seen a lot of them in their week of hauling, but he did not see why they were crazy. They looked no different even if they were. He hoped the lock-keeper would be asleep, so it would take a while to wake him.

Squelch, squelch-squelch, squelch. The horses kept plodding. Suddenly John caught a break in the rhythm. One foot sounded light. He pushed his way up beside them against the wind and laid a wet hand against a side. He could not see, but the side felt hot and wet, and he got a smell of sweat. Yes, he could feel the off horse limping. Hope filled him. He waited till the boat came up where he was, a small figure, shrunk with cold. The boat's bow, round and sullen, slipped along, the bow light hanging over and showing an old mullein stalk in silhouette against the water.

"Pa!"

His voice was thin against the wind.

He saw his father's figure, rain dripping from the visor of his cap, straight and big, almighty almost, breast to the wind.

"Pa!"

The head turned.

"Hey, there! What you doin'? Get on back! Or I'll soap you proper."

"Pa! Prince has got a limp in his front foot. Pa!"

The voice turned hoarse with passion, "Get on back, you little pup. Fifty-nine's just round the next bend. Take your whip and tar him. Or I'll tar you proper."

John sobbed aloud. For a bare moment he thought of staying still and letting the boat pass on. He would run away and join the railroad.

He would get run over by an engine there, just when things went well, and they would be sorry. He started to draw himself a picture of his body coming home in a black box, and his mother crying, and his father looking ashamed and sorry, and then the lightning made a blue flare and he saw the straight figure of his father ahead, on the *Bacconola*, which seemed struck still, a pill-box in the flat country, and he was afraid and went running desperately, hoping he could get back to the team before he was missed.

He caught the horses on the bend and, lifting his face to the storm, saw the lock lanterns dimly ahead. And even then his ears caught, coming up behind him, the harsh blast of a tin horn.

He looked back and saw a light, two rope lengths behind the *Bacconola*. Even while he watched over his shoulder, he saw that it was creeping up.

"John!" His father's voice beat down the sound of rain. "Lay into them brutes and beat into the lock!"

He could imagine his father glaring back. If only he had not dropped his whip. He would have liked to ask his father for the big bull whip that cracked like forty guns, but he knew what would happen if he did. He shrieked at the horses and fumbled for a stone to throw. But they had heard and recognized the note in his father's voice, and they were bending earnestly against the collars. A sudden excitement filled John as his father's horn rang out for the lock. The wind took the sound and carried it back, and the other boat's horn sounded a double toot for passing. John yelled shrilly. The horses seemed to stand still, and there was an odd effect in the rain of the canal sliding under them inch by inch laboriously, as if with his own feet he turned the world backward.

Minutes crept at them out of the rain, and the lights of the lock did not seem to stir. Then John heard the squelching of the team behind his back. Little by little they were coming up, past the *Bacconola*, until he could hear them panting through the rain, and saw them close behind, behind dim puffs of steamy breath. He watched them frantically. Then the lightning came once more, a triple bolt, and the thunder shook him, and when he opened his eyes once more he saw the lock lanterns a hundred yards ahead.

At that instant the driver of the boat behind yelled, "Haw!" and the following team swung across his towrope, and they were snarled.

The horses stopped of themselves, shuddering. They were old

hands, and knew enough not to move, for fear of being thrown from the towpath. The boats came drifting on, placidly as water-logged sticks. The light of the following boat showed a dark bow coming up. John heard his father roaring oaths, and saw by the bow light of the other boat a tall, clean-shaven man as big as his father crouched to jump ashore. Then both boats came in by the towpath, and both men jumped. They made no sound except for the thump of their shoes, but John saw them dim against the lantern light, their fists coming at each other in slow, heavy swings.

The strange team was panting close beside him, and he did not hear the blows landing. There was a pushing upward in his chest, which hurt, and his fists made small balls in the pockets of his trousers. The other boater and his father were standing breast to breast, their faces still, cut, stonelike things in the yellow light, and the rain walling them in. He saw his father lift his hand, and the other man slip, and he would have yelled, for all his cold, if the lightning had not come again, so blue that his eyes smarted. He doubled up, hiding his face, and wept. . . .

A hand caught him by the shoulder.

"A little puny girly boy," said a voice. "I wouldn't lick you proper! Not a little girly baby like you. But I'll spank you just to learn you to let us come by!"

John opened his eyes to see a boy, about his own height but broader built, squinting at him through the rain.

"Take off your pants, dearie," said the boy in a mock voice, digging in his fingers till John winced. "Joe Buller can handle your Captain smart enough. Me, I'll just paddle you to learn you."

John, looking up, was afraid. He did not know what to do, but without warning his hands acted for him, and he struck at the square face with all his might. A pain shot up his arm, making his elbow tingle, and the boy fell back. John could feel the surprise in that body stock still in the rain, and had an instant of astonished pride.

Then panic laid hold of him and he tried to run. But the other boy jumped on his back. They went down flat in the mud, the older boy on John's shoulders, pummeling him till his head sang, and forcing his face into the track, and crying, "Eat it, you lousy little skunk. Eat it, eat it, eat it, eat it."

John could taste the mud in his mouth, with a salty taste, and he began to squirm, twisting his head to escape the brown suffocation.

He heaved himself behind, throwing the boy unexpectedly forward, twisted round, and kicked with all his might. The boy yelled and jumped back on him. And again they went down, this time the boy bent seriously to business. And this time John realized how it was to be hurt. At the third blow something burst loose in his inside and he screamed. He was crying madly. The other boy was heavier, but John squirmed over on his back, and as the brown hand came down on his face he caught it in both his own and bit with all the strength of his jaws. The hand had a slippery, muddy taste, but in a second it was warm in his mouth, and there was a sick, salt warmth on his tongue. The boy struck him once in the eyes and once on the nose, but John held on and bit. Then the boy howled and tore loose and ran back. There was another stroke of lightning, and John saw him doubled up, holding his hand to his mouth; and he got stiffly up, turned his back to the thunder and saw his father bent over the other boater, taking off his shoe.

John walked up to them. His father's face was bleeding a trickle of blood from the right eye into his beard, but he was grinning.

"I'll take his boot for a souvenir," he said. "How'd you come out, Johnny?"

"Oh, pretty good. I guess that other feller won't bother us no more," said John, examining the fallen man. He lay half stunned, by the water's edge, a smooth, big man, with frightened, pale eyes. And one crumpled arm was in the water. John's father looked at the man and then at the boot he had in his hand.

"I'd ought to mark him by the rights of it; but he ain't worth the work, the way he laid down. Who'd ever know his name was Buller?"

Buller. . . . John gazed up admiringly at his big father and studied how the blood ran from the outer corner of the eye and lost its way in the black beard, which the rain had soaked. His father had licked the western bully proper.

"Hey, there!"

The hail came in a thin, cracking voice. Turning, they saw the lock-keeper, white-bearded, peering at them from under the battered umbrella he held with both hands against the wind. The tails of his nightshirt whipped round the tops of his boots.

"Hey, there, you. There'll be some down boats by pretty quick, so you want to hurry along now, while the level's right."

John was aware of his father standing looking down at him.

"Shall we tie-by where we be?" asked his father.

John felt pains coming into the back of his neck where he had been pummeled, and his knuckles ached.

"We can stay here a spell," said his father. "The storm's comin' on again. There'll be bad lightnin' I make no doubt."

As he spoke there came a flash, and John whirled to see if the other driver boy was still visible. He was proud to see him sitting by the towpath, nursing his hurt hand. John did not notice the thunder. He was elaborating a sentence in his mind.

He made a hole in the mud with the toe of his boot, spat into it, and covered it, the way he had seen his father do at home on a Sunday.

"Why," he said, in his high voice, eying the old *Bacconola*, "I guess them poor bezabor farmers will be wantin' them plows for the spring plowing, I guess."

"Me, I'm kind of tuckered," said his father, raising his shoulders to loose the wet shirt off his back. "And the rain's commencing too."

John said importantly, "Watter never hurt a man, it keeps his hide from cracking."

His father jumped aboard. He took his horn and tooted it for the lock. John ran ahead and put back the other boat's team and cried to their own horses to go on. They took up the slack wearily, and presently little ripples showed on the *Bacconola's* bow, and the lantern showed the shore slipping back. On the stern, George Brace blew a blast for the lock. The old lock-keeper was standing by the sluices, drops of water from his beard falling between his feet.

The boat went down, and the horses took it out. Ahead, the team and the boy left the lantern light and entered once more the darkness. The rope followed. And once more the *Bacconola* was alone with its own lantern.

Presently, though, in a stroke of light, George saw his son beside the boat.

"What's the matter? Hey, there!" he asked.

"Say, Pa! Will you chuck me your bull whip here ashore? Them horses is getting kind of dozey. They need soaping proper."

"Where's your whip?"

"I guess I left it a while back. I guess it was in that kind of scrummage we had. I guess it needs a heavier whip anyhow. I guess a man couldn't spare the time going back for it."

"Sure," said George.

He reached down and took it from its peg, recoiled it, and tossed it ashore. The boat went ahead, slowly, with a sound of water, and of rain falling, and of wind.

About the author

Walter D. Edmonds (1903–   ) embarked on a career of chemical engineering at Harvard but quickly discovered that he was not suited for this kind of work. He turned to the study of English, and started writing in earnest when a story of his was accepted for publication by Scribner's Magazine. His first successful novel was a work about the Erie Canal, *Rome Haul.* Since that time, the days of the building of the Erie Canal have become his special field. His *Drums Along the Mohawk* was turned into a highly successful film.

Questions for discussion

1. Is this story about John or about his father? Cite evidence from the story to support your answer.
2. The story begins in the middle of things. For several paragraphs the reader is not certain who the characters are, or where they are. Then, in a flashback, the information is given. Find this flashback. What does it tell the reader?
3. Early in the story, John's father says, "Watter never hurt a man." Why did he say this? Later in the story, John himself repeats the words. Why?
4. The story shows a great change that takes place in John. What is he thinking about at the beginning of the story? What is he thinking about at the end? What is the change, then, in John?
5. How does the writer make the sudden change in John seem reasonable? When is the reader definitely sure that John is going to "give what it takes" to get the boat into Syracuse?
6. Can you admire a person and still be afraid of him? John feared his father. Find examples of this. Did John also admire his father? Cite evidence from the story.
7. Was George Brace another bully like the man he had defeated? Did he have certain admirable qualities? What sort of a father was he? Just as they had a chance to get into the lock, "John was aware of his father standing and looking at him." What was the father thinking? Give proof for your answer.
8. There are several conflicts in the story: the fight between the Braces and the other boat; the conflict between John and his father; the

conflict between John and the demands of his job; the conflict within John himself. Which of these is the major conflict, and the basis of the plot? Point out the ups and downs that make the outcome of the major conflict uncertain. At what point is this conflict settled?

9. What is the theme of this story? What is the story basically about? (It is not about a fight on the Erie Canal.)

10. SETTING. The setting of a story includes the historical period in which it takes place, the geographical area where it occurs, the place of the action, the weather and the time of day. In some stories the setting is important; in others, it is not. How can you tell? The setting is important if the story could not have happened at any other time and place. In some stories, the author gives additional importance to the setting by making the story's outcome depend upon it.

In "The Sea Devil," the setting of the Florida coast is very important. The story could not have easily taken place elsewhere. But even more important, the net, the water-soaked posts, the dark, lonesome night, and even the fish themselves are essential parts of the story.

a. In what other stories that you have read in this book is setting particularly important?

b. In what way is the setting important in "Water Never Hurt a Man"?

Vocabulary growth

CONTEXT. When you are reading a story as exciting as "Water Never Hurt a Man," you do not want to stop to look up words in a dictionary. If you meet a new word, you can make a check mark in the margin and look the word up later. But if the word is important in the story, you may be missing something. It is better to make a guess than to ignore the word completely. This is the point at which context clues help you. They will not tell you everything about the word, but they may give you enough meaning so that you can get on with your reading.

In "Water Never Hurt a Man," the word *bow* is important, and there are context clues that give you all the meaning you need. You know the word as a verb meaning "to bend the body." You also know the word in the phrase "bow and arrows," and you know its meaning in the phrase "ribbons and bows." But none of these meanings fit *bow* as it is used in this story.

We first meet the word in the sentence, "He could barely make out the *bow* lantern." Then again on page 125 another boat came by "with its *bow* light a yellow torch against the rain."

From these two uses, we might think that *bow* refers to a kind of light. But now on page 125 we get another clue: "The boat's *bow*, round and sullen, slipped along . . ." From this sentence, we know that a *bow* is part of a boat. But which part of a boat is it?

Two other clues tell us. On page 127 we read, "The light of the following boat showed a dark *bow* coming up." Obviously, it would be the front part of a boat that you would see coming up behind you.

There are other clues in the story, but those mentioned are enough. While reading "Water Never Hurt a Man," all you need to know is that a *bow* is part of a boat. By the way, how is the word pronounced? Context will not tell, but a dictionary will.

On page 129 we read, "He was *elaborating* a sentence in his mind." From the context, figure out a meaning for *elaborating* that fits the sentence.

For composition

1. Writers of historical fiction do a great deal of research before they write their stories and novels. What can you learn from good historical fiction that you do not learn from a straight history text? Write a paragraph to explain. Cite specific examples from "Water Never Hurt a Man."

2. You are a reporter on a Syracuse newspaper. You have heard rumors of the fight between Brace and Buller. You must investigate the facts and write an account of the story. Your lead is: "The long, brutal reign of Buffalo Joe Buller came to an end last night on the rain-soaked banks of the canal below this city."

The Secret Life of Walter Mitty

JAMES THURBER

There is adventure in the life of an airplane pilot, in the life of a surgeon, in the trial experiences of a criminal lawyer. Here is a story of adventure—with a difference.

"WE'RE going through!" The Commander's voice was like thin ice breaking. He wore his full-dress uniform, with the heavily braided white cap pulled down rakishly over one cold gray eye. "We can't make it, sir. It's spoiling for a hurricane, if you ask me." "I'm not asking you, Lieutenant Berg," said the Commander. "Throw on the power lights! Rev her up to 8,500! We're going through!" The pounding of the cylinders increased: ta-pocketa-pocketa-pocketa-*pocketa-pocketa*. The Commander stared at the ice forming on the pilot window. He walked over and twisted a row of complicated dials. "Switch on No. 8 auxiliary!" he shouted. "Switch on No. 8 auxiliary!" repeated Lieutenant Berg. "Full strength in No. 3 turret!" shouted the Commander. "Full strength in No. 3 turret!" The crew, bending to their various tasks in the huge, hurtling eight-engined Navy hydroplane, looked at each other and grinned. "The Old Man'll get us through," they said to one another. "The Old Man ain't afraid of Hell!" . . .

"Not so fast! You're driving too fast!" said Mrs. Mitty. "What are you driving so fast for?"

"Hmm?" said Walter Mitty. He looked at his wife, in the seat beside him, with shocked astonishment. She seemed grossly unfamiliar, like a strange woman who had yelled at him in a crowd. "You were up to fifty-five," she said. "You know I don't like to go more than forty. You were up to fifty-five." Walter Mitty drove on toward Waterbury in silence, the roaring of the SN202 through the worst storm in twenty years of Navy flying fading in the remote, intimate airways of his mind. "You're tensed up again," said Mrs. Mitty. "It's one of your days. I wish you'd let Dr. Renshaw look you over."

Walter Mitty stopped the car in front of the building where his wife went to have her hair done. "Remember to get those overshoes while I'm having my hair done," she said. "I don't need overshoes," said Mitty. She put her mirror back into her bag. "We've been through that," she said, getting out of the car. "You're not a young man any longer." He raced the engine a little. "Why don't you wear your gloves? Have you lost your gloves?" Walter Mitty reached in a pocket and brought out the gloves. He put them on, but after she had turned and gone into the building and he had driven on to a red light, he took them off again. "Pick it up, brother!" snapped a cop as the light changed, and Mitty hastily pulled on his gloves and lurched ahead. He drove around the streets aimlessly for a time, and then he drove past the hospital on his way to the parking lot.

. . . "It's the millionaire banker, Wellington McMillan," said the pretty nurse. "Yes?" said Walter Mitty, removing his gloves slowly. "Who has the case?" "Dr. Renshaw and Dr. Benbow, but there are two specialists here, Dr. Remington from New York and Dr. Pritchard-Mitford from London. He flew over." A door opened down a long, cool corridor and Dr. Renshaw came out. He looked distraught and haggard. "Hello, Mitty," he said. "We're having the devil's own time with McMillan, the millionaire banker and close personal friend of Roosevelt. Obstreosis of the ductal tract. Tertiary. Wish you'd take a look at him." "Glad to," said Mitty.

In the operating room there were whispered introductions: "Dr. Remington, Dr. Mitty. Dr. Pritchard-Mitford, Dr. Mitty." "I've read your book on streptothricosis," said Pritchard-Mitford, shaking hands. "A brilliant performance, sir." "Thank you," said Walter Mitty. "Didn't know you were in the states, Mitty," grumbled Remington. "Coals to Newcastle, bringing Mitford and me up here for a tertiary." "You are very kind," said Mitty. A huge, complicated machine, connected to the operating table, with many tubes and wires, began at this moment to go pocketa-pocketa-pocketa. "The new anaesthetizer is giving away!" shouted an intern. "There is no one in the East who knows how to fix it!" "Quiet, man!" said Mitty, in a low, cool voice. He sprang to the machine, which was now going pocketa-pocketa-queep-pocketa-queep. He began fingering delicately a row of glistening dials. "Give me a fountain pen!" he snapped. Someone handed him a fountain pen. He pulled a faulty piston out of the machine and inserted the pen in its place. "That will hold for ten minutes," he said. "Get on with the operation." A nurse hurried over and whispered to Renshaw, and Mitty saw the man turn pale. "Coreopsis has set in," said Renshaw nervously. "If you would take over, Mitty?" Mitty looked at him and at the craven figure of Benbow, who drank, and at the grave, uncertain faces of the two great specialists. "If you wish," he said. They slipped a white gown on him; he adjusted a mask and drew on thin gloves; nurses handed him shining . . .

"Back it up, Mac! Look out for that Buick!" Walter Mitty jammed on the brakes. "Wrong lane, Mac," said the parking-lot attendant, looking at Mitty closely. "Gee. Yeh," muttered Mitty. He began cautiously to back out of the lane marked "Exit Only." "Leave her sit there," said the attendant. "I'll put her away." Mitty got out of the car. "Hey, better leave the key." "Oh," said Mitty, handing the man the ignition key. The attendant vaulted into the car, backed it up with insolent skill, and put it where it belonged.

They're so darn cocky, thought Walter Mitty, walking along Main Street; they think they know everything. Once he had tried to take his chains off, outside New Milford, and he had got them wound around the axles. A man had had to come out in a wrecking car and unwind them, a young, grinning garageman. Since then Mrs. Mitty always made him drive to a garage to have the chains taken off. The next time, he thought, I'll wear my right arm in a sling; they won't grin at me then. I'll have my right arm in a sling and they'll see I couldn't possibly take the chains off myself. He kicked at the slush on the sidewalk. "Overshoes," he said to himself and he began looking for a shoe store.

When he came out into the street again, with the overshoes in a box under his arm, Walter Mitty began to wonder what the other thing was his wife had told him to get. She had told him twice before they set out from their house for Waterbury. In a way he hated these weekly trips to town—he was always getting something wrong. Kleenex, he thought. Squibb's, razor blades? No. Toothpaste, toothbrush, bicarbonate, carborundum, initiative and referendum? He gave it up. But she would remember it. "Where's the what's-its-name?" she would ask. "Don't tell me you forgot the what's-its-name." A newsboy went by shouting something about the Waterbury trial.

. . . "Perhaps this will refresh your memory." The District Attorney suddenly thrust a heavy automatic at the quiet figure on the witness stand. "Have you ever seen this before?" Walter Mitty took the gun and examined it expertly. "This is my Webley-Vickers 50.80," he said calmly. An excited buzz ran around the courtroom. The Judge rapped for order. "You are a crack shot with any sort of firearms, I believe?" said the District Attorney, insinuatingly. "Objection!" shouted Mitty's attorney. "We have shown that the defendant could not have fired the shot. We have shown that he wore his right arm in a sling on the night of the fourteenth of July." Walter Mitty raised his hand briefly and the bickering attorneys were stilled. "With any known make of gun," he said evenly, "I could have killed Gregory Fitzhurst at three hundred feet *with my left hand*." Pandemonium broke loose in the courtroom. A woman's scream rose above the bedlam and suddenly a lovely, dark-haired girl was in Walter Mitty's arms. The District Attorney struck at her savagely. Without rising from his chair, Mitty let the man have it on the point of the chin. "You miserable cur!" . . .

"Puppy biscuit," said Walter Mitty. He stopped walking and the buildings of Waterbury rose up out of the misty courtroom and surrounded him again. A woman who was passing laughed. "He said 'Puppy biscuit,' " she said to her companion. "That man said 'Puppy biscuit' to himself." Walter Mitty hurried on. He went into an A. & P., not the first one he came to but a smaller one farther up the street. "I want some biscuit for small, young dogs," he said to the clerk. "Any special brand, sir?" The greatest pistol shot in the world thought a moment. "It says 'Puppies Bark for It' on the box," said Walter Mitty.

His wife would be through at the hairdresser's in fifteen minutes, Mitty saw in looking at his watch, unless they had trouble drying it; sometimes they had trouble drying it. She didn't like to get to the hotel first; she would want him to be there waiting for her as usual. He found a big leather chair in the lobby, facing a window, and he put the overshoes and the puppy biscuit on the floor beside it. He picked up an old copy of *Liberty* and sank down into the chair. "Can Germany Conquer the World Through the Air?" Walter Mitty looked at the pictures of bombing planes and of ruined streets.

. . . "The cannonading has got the wind up in young Raleigh, sir," said the sergeant. Captain Mitty looked up at him through tousled hair. "Get him to bed," he said wearily, "with the others. I'll fly alone." "But you can't, sir," said the sergeant anxiously. "It takes two men to handle that bomber and the Archies are pounding hell out of the air. Von Richtman's circus is between here and Saulier." "Somebody's got to get that ammunition dump," said Mitty. "I'm going over. Spot of brandy?" He poured a drink for the sergeant and one for himself. War thundered and whined around the dugout and battered at the door. There was a rending of wood, and splinters flew through the room. "A bit of a near thing," said Captain Mitty carelessly. "The box barrage is closing in," said the sergeant. "We only live once, Sergeant," said Mitty, with his faint, fleeting smile. "Or do we?" He poured another brandy and tossed it off. "I never see a man could hold his brandy like you, sir," said the sergeant. "Begging your pardon, sir." Captain Mitty stood up and strapped on his huge Webley-Vickers automatic. "It's forty kilometres through hell, sir," said the sergeant. Mitty finished one last brandy. "After all," he said softly, "what isn't?" The pounding of the cannon increased; there was the rat-tat-tatting of machine guns, and from somewhere came the menacing pocketa-pocketa-pocketa of the new flame throwers. Walter Mitty walked to the door of the dugout humming "Auprès de Ma Blonde." He turned and waved to the sergeant. "Cheerio!" he said. . . .

Something struck his shoulder. "I've been looking all over this hotel for you," said Mrs. Mitty. "Why do you have to hide in this old chair? How did you expect me to find you?" "Things close in," said Walter Mitty vaguely. "What?" Mrs. Mitty said. "Did you get the what's-its-name? The puppy biscuit? What's in that box?" "Overshoes," said Mitty. "Couldn't you have put them on in the store?" "I was thinking," said Walter Mitty. "Does it ever occur to you that I am sometimes thinking?" She looked at him. "I'm going to take your temperature when I get you home," she said.

They went out through the revolving doors that made a faintly derisive whistling sound when you pushed them. It was two blocks to the parking lot. At the drugstore on the corner she said, "Wait here for me. I forgot something. I won't be a minute." She was more than a minute. Walter Mitty lighted a cigarette. It began to rain, rain with sleet in it. He stood up against the wall of the drugstore smoking. . . . He put his shoulders back and his heels together. "To hell with the handkerchief," said Walter Mitty scornfully. He took one last drag on his cigarette and snapped it away. Then, with that faint, fleeting smile playing about his lips, he faced the firing squad; erect and motionless, proud and disdainful, Walter Mitty, the Undefeated, inscrutable to the last.

About the author

James Thurber (1894–   ) is known as a humorist, but his readers should not be misled by this reputation, for he is also a serious commentator on American life. Primarily an essayist and short story writer, he has also collaborated on stage plays, and has appeared as an actor in *The Thurber Carnival*, playing the part of James Thurber. In his later years, he suffered an impairment of his eyesight, but nearly total blindness has not stopped his creative outflow.

Questions for discussion

1. The story begins realistically like any good action story about flying. At what point did you first realize that this was not a real action story?
2. Would the daydreams of most people have such a wide variety as Mitty's? Mitty's daydreams reveal an amazing range of technical understanding, a rich vocabulary, and a deeply dramatic quality. Cite instances of each of these from the story.
3. Is there any evidence in the story that would lead you to believe that Mitty has a practical, as well as a romantic streak?
4. When is daydreaming useful and wholesome? When is it undesirable? Do Mitty's daydreams hurt him or others in any way? Compare Mitty's daydreams to Molly Morgan's. How are they alike? How do they differ?
5. What is the author's attitude toward Mitty? Is he making fun of Mitty? Is he sympathetic? Give proof of your answer from the story.
6. One of the amusing contrasts of the story is the dramatic quality of Mitty's daydreams played against the practical concerns of Mrs. Mitty. Point out examples.
7. Is the conflict in this story external—between Mitty and his wife? Internal—within Mitty himself? Upon what do you base your answer?

Vocabulary growth

CONTEXT. On page 134 you read, "A door opened down a long cool corridor and Dr. Renshaw came out. He looked *distraught* and *haggard.* 'Hello, Mitty,' he said. 'We're having the devil's own time with McMillan . . . Wish you'd take a look at him.' "

What does "distraught and haggard" mean? How much meaning can you get from the context? You know from the story that this is another case of "Mitty to the rescue." Obviously, he would not be rescuing someone happy, content, comfortable, and at ease. You can deduce, therefore, that "distraught" and "haggard" refer to something unpleasant. Note that the doctor *looked* distraught and haggard. The words describe appearance. Can you now deduce how the doctor must have looked?

    a. On page 136 occurs the sentence, "Walter Mitty raised his hand briefly and the *bickering* attorneys were stilled." Reread the paragraph and from context clues work out the meaning of *bickering*.

    b. In the same paragraph occur the words *pandemonium* and *bedlam*. Work out their meaning from the context.

WORDS ARE INTERESTING. The word *bedlam* comes from Bethlehem Hospital in London long ago, where mentally ill people were treated. The name *Bethlehem* came to be shortened to *bedlam* from frequent use. The noise of the patients became associated with the word.

In *pandemonium*, the prefix *pan-* means "all." The suffix *-ium* often means "a place where," as in *aquarium* and *planetarium*. Thus, *Pandemonium* is the place where all demons dwell, a place of noise and confusion.

For composition

1. Everyone goes through unpleasant situations, such as explaining a car smashup, being turned down for a job, being criticized for doing poor work. Perhaps you have had such an experience recently. Write two accounts of the situation. In the first, report what actually happened. Then write an account of how you would have handled the situation so that you would have come out well.

2. If dreams are to come true, people must do something to make them come true. Write a short biographical sketch of some person who made a dream come true. The person might be yourself, or some well-known personality whom all the class will recognize.

3. This story is written from the point of view of an observer, in the third person. To get an idea of how important point of view is, try rewriting one of Mitty's daydreams in the first person. For example: ". . . 'It's the millionaire banker, Wellington McMillan,' said the pretty nurse. 'Yes?' I said, removing my gloves . . ."

One Ordinary Day, with Peanuts

SHIRLEY JACKSON

You will have fun reading this story. Somewhere along the way you will decide that something very odd is going on here, and that the story expresses a serious idea. Suppose that you didn't have to go to work. Suppose that you had enough money to do what you wanted. Suppose. . . .

MR. John Philip Johnson shut his front door behind him and came down his front steps in the bright morning with a feeling that all was well with the world on this best of all days, and wasn't the sun warm and good, and didn't his shoes feel comfortable after the resoling, and he knew that he had undoubtedly chosen the precise very tie which belonged with the day and the sun and his comfortable feet, and, after all, wasn't the world just a wonderful place? In spite of the fact that he was a small man, and the tie was perhaps a shade vivid, Mr. Johnson irradiated this feeling of well-being as he came down the steps and onto the dirty sidewalk, and he smiled at people who passed him, and some of them even smiled back. He stopped at the newsstand on the corner and bought his paper, saying "Good morning" with real conviction to the man who sold him the paper and the two or three other people who were lucky enough to be buying papers when Mr. Johnson skipped up. He remembered to fill his pockets with candy and peanuts, and then he set out to get himself uptown. He stopped in a flower shop and bought a carnation for his buttonhole, and stopped almost immediately afterward to give the carnation to a small child in a carriage, who looked at him dumbly, and then smiled, and Mr. Johnson smiled, and the child's mother looked at Mr. Johnson for a minute and then smiled too.

When he had gone several blocks uptown, Mr. Johnson cut across the avenue and went along a side street, chosen at random; he did not follow the same route every morning, but preferred to pursue his eventful way in wide detours, more like a puppy than a man intent upon business. It happened this morning that halfway down the block a moving van was parked, and the furniture from an upstairs apartment stood half on the sidewalk, half on the steps, while an amused group of people loitered, examining the scratches on the tables and the worn spots on the chairs, and a harassed woman, trying to watch a young child and the movers and the furniture all at the same time, gave the clear impression of endeavoring to shelter her private life from the people staring at her belongings. Mr. Johnson stopped, and for a moment joined the crowd, and then he came forward and, touching his hat civilly, said, "Perhaps I can keep an eye on your little boy for you?"

The woman turned and glared at him distrustfully, and Mr. Johnson added hastily, "We'll sit right here on the steps." He beckoned to the little boy, who hesitated and then responded agreeably to Mr. Johnson's genial smile. Mr. Johnson brought out a handful of peanuts from his pocket and sat on the steps with the boy, who at first refused the peanuts on the grounds that his mother did not allow him to accept food from strangers; Mr. Johnson said that probably his mother had not intended peanuts to be included, since elephants at the circus ate them, and the boy considered, and then agreed solemnly. They sat on the steps cracking peanuts in a comradely fashion, and Mr. Johnson said, "So you're moving?"

"Yep," said the boy.

"Where you going?"

"Vermont."

"Nice place. Plenty of snow there. Maple sugar, too; you like maple sugar?"

"Sure."

"Plenty of maple sugar in Vermont. You going to live on a farm?"

"Going to live with Grandpa."

"Grandpa like peanuts?"

"Sure."

"Ought to take him some," said Mr. Johnson, reaching into his pocket. "Just you and Mommy going?"

"Yep."

"Tell you what," Mr. Johnson said. "You take some peanuts to eat on the train."

The boy's mother, after glancing at them frequently, had seemingly decided that Mr. Johnson was trustworthy, because she had devoted herself wholeheartedly to seeing that the movers did not— what movers rarely do, but every housewife believes they will—crack a leg from her good table, or set a kitchen chair down on a lamp. Most of the furniture was loaded by now, and she was deep in that nervous stage when she knew there was something she had forgotten to pack—hidden away in the back of a closet somewhere, or left at a neighbor's and forgotten, or on the clothesline—and was trying to remember under stress what it was.

"This all, lady?" the chief mover said, completing her dismay.

Uncertainly, she nodded.

"Want to go on the truck with the furniture, sonny?" the mover asked the boy, and laughed. The boy laughed too and said to Mr. Johnson, "I guess I'll have a good time at Vermont."

"Fine time," said Mr. Johnson, and stood up. "Have one more peanut before you go," he said to the boy.

The boy's mother said to Mr. Johnson, "Thank you so much; it was a great help to me."

"Nothing at all," said Mr. Johnson gallantly. "Where in Vermont are you going?"

The mother looked at the little boy accusingly, as though he had given away a secret of some importance, and said unwillingly, "Greenwich."

"Lovely town," said Mr. Johnson. He took out a card, and wrote a name on the back. "Very good friend of mine lives in Greenwich," he said. "Call on him for anything you need. His wife makes the best doughnuts in town," he added soberly to the little boy.

"Swell," said the little boy.

"Goodbye," said Mr. Johnson.

He went on, stepping happily with his new-shod feet, feeling the warm sun on his back and on the top of his head. Halfway down the block he met a stray dog and fed him a peanut.

At the corner, where another wide avenue faced him, Mr. Johnson decided to go on uptown again. Moving with comparative laziness, he was passed on either side by people hurrying and frowning, and people brushed past him going the other way, clattering along to get somewhere quickly. Mr. Johnson stopped on every corner and waited patiently for the light to change, and he stepped out of the way of anyone who seemed to be in any particular hurry, but one young lady came too fast for him, and crashed wildly into him when he stooped to pat a kitten which had run out onto the sidewalk from an apartment house and was now unable to get back through the rushing feet.

"Excuse me," said the young lady, trying frantically to pick up Mr. Johnson and hurry on at the same time, "terribly sorry."

The kitten, regardless now of danger, raced back to its home.

"Perfectly all right," said Mr. Johnson, adjusting himself carefully. "You seem to be in a hurry."

"Of course I'm in a hurry," said the young lady. "I'm late."

She was extremely cross and the frown between her eyes seemed well on its way to becoming permanent. She had obviously awakened late, because she had not spent any extra time in making herself look pretty, and her dress was plain and unadorned with collar or brooch, and her lipstick was noticeably crooked. She tried to brush past Mr. Johnson, but, risking her suspicious displeasure, he took her arm and said, "Please wait."

"Look," she said ominously, "I ran into you and your lawyer can see my lawyer and I will gladly pay all damages and all inconveniences suffered therefrom but please this minute let me go because *I am late.*"

"Late for what?" said Mr. Johnson; he tried his winning smile on her but it did no more than keep her, he suspected, from knocking him down again.

"Late for work," she said between her teeth. "Late for my employment. I have a job and if I am late I lose exactly so much an hour and I cannot really afford what your pleasant conversation is costing me, be it *ever* so pleasant."

"I'll pay for it," said Mr. Johnson. Now these were magic words, not necessarily because they were true, or because she seriously expected Mr. Johnson to pay for anything, but because Mr. Johnson's flat statement, obviously innocent of irony, could not be, coming from Mr. Johnson, anything but the statement of a responsible and truthful and respectable man.

"What *do* you mean?" she asked.

"I said that since I am obviously responsible for your being late I shall certainly pay for it."

"Don't be silly," she said, and for the first time the frown disappeared. "I wouldn't expect you to pay for anything—a few minutes ago I was offering to pay *you.* Anyway," she added, almost smiling, "it *was* my fault."

"What happens if you don't go to work?"

She stared. "I don't get paid."

"Precisely," said Mr. Johnson.

"What do you mean, precisely? If I don't show up at the office exactly twenty minutes ago I lose a dollar and twenty cents an hour, or two cents a minute or . . ." she thought. ". . . Almost a dime for the time I've spent talking to you."

Mr. Johnson laughed, and finally she laughed, too. "You're late already," he pointed out. "Will you give me another four cents worth?"

"I don't understand why."

"You'll see," Mr. Johnson promised. He led her over to the side of the walk, next to the buildings, and said, "Stand here," and went out into the rush of people going both ways. Selecting and considering, as one who must make a choice involving perhaps whole years of lives, he estimated the people going by. Once he almost moved, and then at the last minute thought better of it and drew back. Finally, from half a block away, he saw what he wanted, and moved out into the center of the traffic to intercept a young man, who was hurrying, and dressed as though he had awakened late, and frowning.

"Oof," said the young man, because Mr. Johnson had thought of no better way to intercept anyone than the one the young woman had unwittingly used upon him. "Where do you think you're going?" the young man demanded from the sidewalk.

"I want to speak to you," said Mr. Johnson ominously.

The young man got up nervously, dusting himself and eying Mr. Johnson. "What for?" he said. "What'd *I* do?"

"That's what bothers me most about people nowadays," Mr. Johnson complained broadly to the people passing. "No matter whether they've done anything or not, they always figure someone's after them. About what you're going to do," he told the young man.

"Listen," said the young man, trying to brush past him, "I'm late, and I don't have any time to listen. Here's a dime, now get going."

"Thank you," said Mr. Johnson, pocketing the dime. "Look," he said, "what happens if you stop running?"

"I'm late," said the young man, still trying to get past Mr. Johnson, who was unexpectedly clinging.

"How much you make an hour?" Mr. Johnson demanded.

"A communist, are you?" said the young man. "Now will you please let me—"

"No," said Mr. Johnson insistently, "*how* much?"

"Dollar fifty," said the young man. "And *now* will you—"

"You like adventure?"

The young man stared, and, staring, found himself caught and held by Mr. Johnson's genial smile; he almost smiled back and then repressed it and made an effort to tear away. "I got to *hurry*," he said.

"Mystery? Like surprises? Unusual and exciting events?"

"You selling something?"

"Sure," said Mr. Johnson. "You want to take a chance?"

The young man hesitated, looked longingly up the avenue toward what might have been his destination and then, when Mr. Johnson said "I'll pay for it" with his own peculiar convincing emphasis, turned and said, "Well, okay. But I got to *see* it first, what I'm buying."

Mr. Johnson, breathing hard, led the young man over to the side where the girl was standing; she had been watching with interest Mr. Johnson's capture of the young man and now, smiling timidly, she looked at Mr. Johnson as though prepared to be surprised at nothing.

Mr. Johnson reached into his pocket and took out his wallet. "Here," he said, and handed a bill to the girl. "This about equals your day's pay."

"But no," she said, surprised in spite of herself. "I mean, I *couldn't*."

"Please do not interrupt," Mr. Johnson told her. "And *here*," he said to the young man, "this will take care of *you*." The young man accepted the bill dazedly, but said, "Probably counterfeit" to the young woman out of the side of his mouth. "Now," Mr. Johnson went on, disregarding the young man, "what is your name, miss?"

"Kent," she said helplessly. "Mildred Kent."

"Fine," said Mr. Johnson. "And you, sir?"

"Arthur Adams," said the young man stiffly.

"Splendid," said Mr. Johnson. "Now, Miss Kent, I would like you to meet Mr. Adams. Mr. Adams, Miss Kent."

Miss Kent stared, wet her lips nervously, made a gesture as though she might run, and said, "How do you do?"

Mr. Adams straightened his shoulders, scowled at Mr. Johnson, made a gesture as though he might run, and said, "How do you do?"

"Now *this*," said Mr. Johnson, taking several bills from his wallet, "should be enough for the day for both of you. I would suggest, perhaps, Coney Island—although I personally am not fond of the place—or perhaps a nice lunch somewhere, and dancing, or a matinee, or even a movie, although take care to choose a really *good* one; there are *so* many bad movies these days. You might," he said, struck with an inspiration, "visit the Bronx Zoo, or the Planetarium. Anywhere, as a matter of fact," he concluded, "that you would like to go. Have a nice time."

As he started to move away Arthur Adams, breaking from his dumbfounded stare, said, "But see here, mister, you *can't* do this. Why—how do you know—I mean, *we* don't even know—I mean, how do you know we won't just take the money and not do what you said?"

"You've taken the money," Mr. Johnson said. "You don't have to follow any of my suggestions. You may know something you prefer to do—perhaps a museum, or something."

"But suppose I just run away with it and leave her here?"

"I know you won't," said Mr. Johnson gently, "because you remembered to ask *me* that. Goodbye," he added, and went on.

As he stepped up the street, conscious of the sun on his head and his good shoes, he heard from somewhere behind him the young man saying, "Look, you know you don't *have* to if you don't want to," and the girl saying, "But unless *you* don't want to . . . " Mr. Johnson smiled to himself and then thought that he had better hurry along; when he wanted to he could move very quickly, and before the young woman had gotten around to saying, "Well, *I* will if *you* will," Mr. Johnson was several blocks away and had already stopped twice, once to help a lady lift several large packages into a taxi and once to hand a peanut to a seagull. By this time he was in an area of large stores and many more people and he was buffeted constantly from either side by people hurrying and cross and late and sullen. Once he offered a peanut to a man who asked him for a dime, and once he offered a peanut to a bus driver who had stopped his bus at an intersection and had opened the window next to his seat and put out his head as though longing for fresh air and the comparative quiet of the traffic. The man wanting a dime took the peanut because Mr. Johnson had wrapped a dollar bill around it, but the bus driver took the peanut and asked ironically, "You want a transfer, Jack?"

On a busy corner Mr. Johnson encountered two young people— for one minute he thought they might be Mildred Kent and Arthur Adams—who were eagerly scanning a newspaper, their backs pressed against a storefront to avoid the people passing, their heads bent together. Mr. Johnson, whose curiosity was insatiable, leaned onto the storefront next to them and peeked over the man's shoulder; they were scanning the "Apartments Vacant" columns.

Mr. Johnson remembered the street where the woman and her little boy were going to Vermont and he tapped the man on the shoulder and said amiably, "Try down on West Seventeen. About the middle of the block, people moved out this morning."

"Say, what do you—" said the man, and then, seeing Mr. Johnson clearly, "Well, thanks. Where did you say?"

"West Seventeen," said Mr. Johnson. "About the middle of the block." He smiled again and said, "Good luck."

"Thanks," said the man.

"Thanks," said the girl, as they moved off.

"Goodbye," said Mr. Johnson.

He lunched alone in a pleasant restaurant, where the food was rich, and only Mr. Johnson's excellent digestion could encompass two of their whipped-cream-and-chocolate-and-rum-cake pastries for dessert. He had three cups of coffee, tipped the waiter largely, and went out into the street again into the wonderful sunlight, his shoes still comfortable and fresh on his feet. Outside he found a beggar staring into the windows of the restaurant he had left and, carefully looking through the money in his pocket, Mr. Johnson approached the beggar and pressed some coins and a couple of bills into his hand. "It's the price of the veal cutlet lunch plus tip," said Mr. Johnson. "Goodbye."

After his lunch he rested; he walked into the nearest park and fed peanuts to the pigeons. It was late afternoon by the time he was ready to start back downtown, and he had refereed two checker games and watched a small boy and girl whose mother had fallen asleep and awakened with surprise and fear which turned to amusement when she saw Mr. Johnson. He had given away almost all of his candy, and had fed all the rest of his peanuts to the pigeons, and it was time to go home. Although the late afternoon sun was pleasant, and his shoes were still entirely comfortable, he decided to take a taxi downtown.

He had a difficult time catching a taxi, because he gave up the first three or four empty ones to people who seemed to need them more; finally, however, he stood alone on the corner and—almost like netting a frisky fish—he hailed desperately until he succeeded in catching a cab which had been proceeding with haste uptown and seemed to draw in toward Mr. Johnson against its own will.

"Mister," the cab driver said as Mr. Johnson climbed in, "I figured you was an omen, like. I wasn't going to pick you up at all."

"Kind of you," said Mr. Johnson ambiguously.

"If I'd of let you go it would of cost me ten bucks," said the driver.

"Really?" said Mr. Johnson.

"Yeah," said the driver. "Guy just got out of the cab, he turned around and give me ten bucks, said take this and bet it in a hurry on a horse named Vulcan, right away."

"Vulcan?" said Mr. Johnson, horrified. "A fire sign on a Wednesday?"

"What?" said the driver. "Anyway, I said to myself if I got no fare between here and there I'd bet the ten, but if anyone looked like they needed the cab I'd take it as a omen and I'd take the ten home to the wife."

"You were very right," said Mr. Johnson heartily. "This is Wednesday, you would have lost your money. Monday, yes, or even Saturday. But never never never a fire sign on a Wednesday. Sunday would have been good, now."

"Vulcan don't run on Sunday," said the driver.

"You wait till another day," said Mr. Johnson. "Down this street, please, driver. I'll get off on the next corner."

"He *told* me Vulcan, though," said the driver.

"I'll tell you," said Mr. Johnson, hesitating with the door of the cab half open. "You take that ten dollars and I'll give you another ten dollars to go with it, and you go right ahead and bet that money on any Thursday on any horse that has a name indicating . . . let me see, Thursday . . . well, grain. Or any growing food."

"Grain?" said the driver. "You mean a horse named, like, Wheat or something?"

"Certainly," said Mr. Johnson. "Or, as a matter of fact, to make it even easier, any horse whose name includes the letters C, R, L. Perfectly simple."

"Tall corn?" said the driver, a light in his eye. "You mean a horse named, like, Tall Corn?"

"Absolutely," said Mr. Johnson. "Here's your money."

"Tall Corn," said the driver. "Thank *you*, mister."

"Goodbye," said Mr. Johnson.

He was on his own corner and went straight up to his apartment. He let himself in and called "Hello?" and Mrs. Johnson answered from the kitchen, "Hello, dear, aren't you early?"

"Took a taxi home," Mr. Johnson said. "I remembered the cheese-cake, too. What's for dinner?"

Mrs. Johnson came out of the kitchen and kissed him; she was a comfortable woman, and smiling as Mr. Johnson smiled. "Hard day?" she asked.

"Not very," said Mr. Johnson, hanging his coat in the closet. "How about you?"

"So-so," she said. She stood in the kitchen doorway while he settled into his easy chair and took off his good shoes and took out the paper he had bought that morning. "Here and there," she said.

"I didn't do so badly," Mr. Johnson said. "Couple young people."

"Fine," she said. "I had a little nap this afternoon, took it easy most of the day. Went into a department store this morning and accused the woman next to me of shoplifting, and had the store detective pick her up. Sent three dogs to the pound—*you* know, the usual thing. Oh, and listen," she added, remembering.

"What?" asked Mr. Johnson.

"Well," she said, "I got onto a bus and asked the driver for a transfer, and when he helped someone else first I said that he was impertinent, and quarreled with him. And then I said why wasn't he in the army, and I said it loud enough for everyone to hear, and I took his number and I turned in a complaint. Probably got him fired."

"Fine," said Mr. Johnson. "But you do look tired. Want to change over tomorrow?"

"I *would* like to," she said. "I could do with a change."

"Right," said Mr. Johnson. "What's for dinner?"

"Veal cutlet."

"Had it for lunch," said Mr. Johnson.

About the author

There are two sides to the writing of Shirley Jackson (1919–   ). One side shows her as the mother of a large and happy family, and this side is revealed in informal and humorous essays, as well as in stories like "Charles." The other side of her writing concerns itself with fantasy that is sometimes steeped in horror. "The Lottery," now a modern classic short story, reveals this side of her writing as does her novel *The Bird's Nest.*

Questions for discussion

1. What is the meaning of Mr. Johnson's question on page 149, "Want to change over tomorrow?" What had Mrs. Johnson been doing all day? The changeover takes place at once. How can you tell?

2. What is the significance of Mr. Johnson's saying, "Fine. But you look tired."? Why would he say that the disagreeable things his wife had been doing were fine? What is the scheme or plan upon which the two have been working?

3. When Mr. Johnson says, "You look tired.", what does he mean? Did he get tired from the kind of things he had been doing? What is the author saying here?

4. This story is a *fantasy*. That is, it is not presented as an account of real people meeting real problems. It is all based on an assumption that certain conditions are true. It reports what *might* happen if certain conditions existed. Examine the things that Mr. and Mrs. Johnson did. Were any of them impossible for the average person to do? What would the average person have to do to himself in order to spend a day as Mr. Johnson did? What is the author saying here?

5. The beggar and the man who wanted a dime accepted Mr. Johnson's help. What was the first reaction of the boy? Of the bus driver? Of the young couple looking for an apartment? What is the author saying here about the way people in a big city treat strangers?

6. The incident of Miss Kent and Mr. Adams has a special meaning. What is the author saying here about people in general? "If only people weren't always . . ."

7. Look back to page 33 for an explanation of *irony*. What touch of irony is there in the title of this story? In what way was Mr. Johnson's day "ordinary"? In what way was it not?

8. What is the theme of the story? Your class may not agree. There may be no one right answer, but you should be able to support your own answer by referring to incidents in the story. Write a paragraph in which you state your idea of the theme, with supporting evidence. Read this paragraph aloud to the class, as part of the discussion.

Vocabulary growth

CONTEXT. On page 143 you read, "Now these were magic words, not necessarily because they were true, or because he seriously expected Mr. Johnson to pay for anything, but because Mr. Johnson's flat statement, *innocent* of *irony,* could not be, coming from Mr. Johnson, anything but the statement of a responsible and truthful and respectable man."

a. What does *innocent* mean here?
b. Why was the statement not *ironical?*
c. Under what circumstances could such a statement be *ironical?*

WORDS ARE INTERESTING. *Innocent* has an interesting background. With the aid of your dictionary, find out the background of this word. What base word appears in *innocent?* What other English words also have this base word?

For composition

1. If you liked "One Ordinary Day, with Peanuts," you will like Shirley Jackson's other stories, such as "Charles," "The Lottery," and "Strangers in Town." In "One Ordinary Day," just as in many other of her stories, the author seems to be saying, "Suppose the rules were different? What if people had to obey this kind of rule? Then, how would people behave?" You might like to try a short, short story, or a simple narrative based on this kind of an assumption. For example:
   a. For one day, no one can accept money for anything.
   b. For one day, there is a news blackout. There are no newspapers, no radio and no television.
   c. For one day, everyone goes barefoot.
   d. For one month, John Andrews can decide what the weather will be.

The Feeling of Power

ISAAC ASIMOV

Long, long ago in the 1960's, Earth scientists were building machines to imitate the human brain. In time, they succeeded to a degree. But now, at the time of this story, all of this early work has been forgotten. Men have become dependent upon computers, and there is a certain dissatisfaction with them.

JEHAN Shuman was used to dealing with the men in authority on long-embattled Earth. He was only a civilian but he originated programming patterns that resulted in self-directing war computers of the highest sort. Generals consequently listened to him. Heads of congressional committees, too.

There was one of each in the special lounge of New Pentagon. General Weider was space-burnt and had a small mouth puckered almost into a cipher. Congressman Brant was smooth-cheeked and clear-eyed. He smoked Denebian tobacco with the air of one whose patriotism was so notorious, he could be allowed such liberties.

Shuman, tall, distinguished, and Programmer-first-class, faced them fearlessly.

He said, "This, gentlemen, is Myron Aub."

"The one with the unusual gift that you discovered quite by accident," said Congressman Brant placidly. "Ah." He inspected the little man with the egg-bald head with amiable curiosity.

The little man, in return, twisted the fingers of his hands anxiously. He had never been near such great men before. He was only an aging low-grade Technician who had long ago failed all tests designed to smoke out the gifted ones among mankind and had settled into the rut of unskilled labor. There was just this hobby of his that the great Programmer had found out about and was now making such a frightening fuss over.

General Weider said, "I find this atmosphere of mystery childish."

"You won't in a moment," said Shuman. "This is not something we can leak to the firstcomer. ——Aub!" There was something imperative about his manner of biting off that one-syllable name, but then he was a great Programmer speaking to a mere Technician. "Aub! How much is nine times seven?"

Aub hesitated a moment. His pale eyes glimmered with a feeble anxiety. "Sixty-three," he said.

Congressman Brant lifted his eyebrows. "Is that right?"

"Check it for yourself, Congressman."

The congressman took out his pocket computer, nudged the milled edges twice, looked at its face as it lay there in the palm of his hand, and put it back. He said, "Is this the gift you brought us here to demonstrate. An illusionist?"

"More than that, sir. Aub has memorized a few operations and with them he computes on paper."

"A paper computer?" said the general. He looked pained.

"No, sir," said Shuman patiently. "Not a paper computer. Simply a sheet of paper. General, would you be so kind as to suggest a number?"

"Seventeen," said the general.

"And you, Congressman?"

"Twenty-three."

"Good! Aub, multiply those numbers and please show the gentlemen your manner of doing it."

"Yes, Programmer," said Aub, ducking his head. He fished a small pad out of one shirt pocket and an artist's hairline stylus out of the other. His forehead corrugated as he made painstaking marks on the paper.

General Weider interrupted him sharply. "Let's see that."

Aub passed him the paper, and Weider said, "Well, it looks like the figure seventeen."

Congressman Brant nodded and said, "So it does, but I suppose anyone can copy figures off a computer. I think I could make a passable seventeen myself, even without practice."

"If you will let Aub continue, gentlemen," said Shuman without heat.

Aub continued, his hand trembling a little. Finally he said in a low voice, "The answer is three hundred and ninety-one."

Congressman Brant took out his computer a second time and flicked it, "By Godfrey, so it is. How did he guess?"

"No guess, Congressman," said Shuman. "He computed that result. He did it on this sheet of paper."

"Humbug," said the general impatiently. "A computer is one thing and marks on paper are another."

"Explain, Aub," said Shuman.

"Yes, Programmer. ——Well, gentlemen, I write down seventeen and just underneath it, I write twenty-three. Next, I say to myself: seven times three——"

The congressman interrupted smoothly, "Now, Aub, the problem is seventeen times twenty-three."

"Yes, I know," said the little Technician earnestly, "but I *start* by saying seven times three because that's the way it works. Now seven times three is twenty-one."

"And how do you know that?" asked the congressman.

"I just remember it. It's always twenty-one on the computer. I've checked it any number of times."

"That doesn't mean it always will be, though, does it?" said the congressman.

"Maybe not," stammered Aub. "I'm not a mathematician. But I always get the right answers, you see."

"Go on."

"Seven times three is twenty-one, so I write down twenty-one. Then one times three is three, so I write down a three under the two of twenty-one."

"Why under the two?" asked Congressman Brant at once.

"Because—" Aub looked helplessly at his superior for support. "It's difficult to explain."

Shuman said, "If you will accept his work for the moment, we can leave the details for the mathematicians."

Brant subsided.

Aub said, "Three plus two makes five, you see, so the twenty-one becomes a fifty-one. Now you let that go for a while and start fresh. You multiply seven and two, that's fourteen, and one and two, that's two. Put them down like this and it adds up to thirty-four. Now if you put the thirty-four under the fifty-one this way and add them, you get three hundred and ninety-one and that's the answer."

There was an instant's silence and then General Weider said,

"I don't believe it. He goes through this rigmarole and makes up numbers and multiplies and adds them this way and that, but I don't believe it. It's too complicated to be anything but hornswoggling."

"Oh no, sir," said Aub in a sweat. "It only *seems* complicated because you're not used to it. Actually, the rules are quite simple and will work for any numbers."

"Any numbers, eh?" said the general. "Come then." He took out his own computer (a severely styled GI model) and struck it at random. Make a five seven three eight on the paper. That's five thousand seven hundred and thirty-eight."

"Yes, sir," said Aub, taking a new sheet of paper.

"Now," (more punching of his computer), "seven two three nine. Seven thousand two hundred and thirty-nine."

"Yes, sir."

"And now multiply those two."

"It will take some time," quavered Aub.

"Take the time," said the general.

"Go ahead, Aub," said Shuman crisply.

Aub set to work, bending low. He took another sheet of paper and another. The general took out his watch finally and stared at it. "Are you through with your magic-making, Technician?"

"I'm almost done, sir. ——Here it is, sir. Forty-one million, five hundred and thirty-seven thousand, three hundred and eighty-two." He showed the scrawled figures of the result.

General Weider smiled bitterly. He pushed the multiplication contact on his computer and let the numbers whirl to a halt. And then he stared and said in a surprised squeak, "Great Galaxy, the fella's right."

The President of the Terrestrial Federation had grown haggard in office and, in private, he allowed a look of settled melancholy to appear on his sensitive features. The Denebian war, after its early start of vast movement and great popularity, had trickled down into a sordid matter of maneuver and countermaneuver, with discontent rising steadily on Earth. Possibly, it was rising on Deneb, too.

And now Congressman Brant, head of the important Committee on Military Appropriations was cheerfully and smoothly spending his half-hour appointment spouting nonsense.

"Computing without a computer," said the president impatiently, "is a contradiction in terms."

"Computing," said the congressman, "is only a system for handling data. A machine might do it, or the human brain might. Let me give you an example." And, using the new skills he had learned, he worked out sums and products until the president, despite himself, grew interested.

"Does this always work?"

"Every time, Mr. President. It is foolproof."

"Is it hard to learn?"

"It took me a week to get the real hang of it. I think you would do better."

"Well," said the president, considering, "it's an interesting parlor game, but what is the use of it?"

"What is the use of a newborn baby, Mr. President? At the moment there is no use, but don't you see that this points the way toward liberation from the machine. Consider, Mr. President," the congressman rose and his deep voice automatically took on some of the cadences he used in public debate, "that the Denebian war is a war of computer against computer. Their computers forge an impenetrable shield of counter-missiles against our missiles, and ours forge one against theirs. If we advance the efficiency of our computers, so do they theirs, and for five years a precarious and profitless balance has existed.

"Now we have in our hands a method for going beyond the computer, leapfrogging it, passing through it. We will combine the mechanics of computation with human thought; we will have the equivalent of intelligent computers; billions of them. I can't predict what the consequences will be in detail but they will be incalculable. And if Deneb beats us to the punch, they may be unimaginably catastrophic."

The president said, troubled, "What would you have me do?"

"Put the power of the administration behind the establishment of a secret project on human computation. Call it Project Number, if you like. I can vouch for my committee, but I will need the administration behind me."

"But how far can human computation go?"

"There is no limit. According to Programmer Shuman, who first introduced me to this discovery——"

"I've heard of Shuman, of course."

"Yes. Well, Dr. Shuman tells me that in theory there is nothing the computer can do that the human mind can not do. The computer merely takes a finite amount of data and performs a finite number of operations upon them. The human mind can duplicate the process."

The president considered that. He said, "If Shuman says this, I am inclined to believe him—in theory. But, in practice, how can anyone know how a computer works?"

Brant laughed genially. "Well, Mr. President, I asked the same question. It seems that at one time computers were designed directly by human beings. Those were simple computers, of course, this being before the time of the rational use of computers to design more advanced computers."

"Yes, yes. Go on."

"Technician Aub apparently had, as his hobby, the reconstruction of some of these ancient devices and in so doing he studied the details of their workings and found he could imitate them. The multiplication I just performed for you is an imitation of the workings of a computer."

"Amazing!"

The congressman coughed gently, "If I may make another point, Mr. President—— The further we can develop this thing, the more we can divert our Federal effort from computer production and computer maintenance. As the human brain takes over, more of our energy can be directed into peacetime pursuits and the impingement of war on the ordinary man will be less. This will be most advantageous for the party in power, of course."

"Ah," said the president, "I see your point. Well, sit down, Congressman, sit down. I want some time to think about this. ——But meanwhile, show me that multiplication trick again. Let's see if I can't catch the point of it."

Programmer Shuman did not try to hurry matters. Loesser was conservative, very conservative, and liked to deal with computers as his father and grandfather had. Still, he controlled the West European computer combine, and if he could be persuaded to join Project Number in full enthusiasm, a great deal would be accomplished.

But Loesser was holding back. He said, "I'm not sure I like the idea of relaxing our hold on computers. The human mind is a capricious thing. The computer will give the same answer to the same problem each time. What guarantee have we that the human mind will do the same?"

"The human mind, Computer Loesser, only manipulates facts. It doesn't matter whether the human mind or a machine does it. They are just tools."

"Yes, yes. I've gone over your ingenious demonstration that the mind can duplicate the computer but it seems to me a little in the air. I'll grant the theory but what reason have we for thinking that theory can be converted to practice?"

"I think we have reason, sir. After all, computers have not always existed. The cave men with their triremes, stone axes, and railroads had no computers."

"And possibly they did not compute."

"You know better than that. Even the building of a railroad or a ziggurat called for some computing, and that must have been without computers as we know them."

"Do you suggest they computed in the fashion you demonstrate?"

"Probably not. After all, this method—we call it 'graphitics,' by the way, from the old European word 'grapho' meaning 'to write'—is developed from the computers themselves so it cannot have antedated them. Still, the cave men must have had *some* method, eh?"

"Lost arts! If you're going to talk about lost arts——"

"No, no. I'm not a lost art enthusiast, though I don't say there may not be some. After all, man was eating grain before hydroponics, and if the primitives ate grain, they must have grown it in soil. What else could they have done?"

"I don't know, but I'll believe in soil-growing when I see someone grow grain in soil. And I'll believe in making fire by rubbing two pieces of flint together when I see that, too."

Shuman grew placative. "Well, let's stick to graphitics. It's just part of the process of etherealization. Transportation by means of bulky contrivances is giving way to direct mass-transference. Communications devices become less massive and more efficient constantly. For that matter, compare your pocket computer with the massive jobs of a thousand years ago. Why not, then, the last step of doing away with computers altogether? Come, sir, Project Number is a going concern; progress is already headlong. But we want your help. If patriotism doesn't move you, consider the intellectual adventure involved."

Loesser said skeptically, "What progress? What can you do beyond multiplication? Can you integrate a transcendental function?"

"In time, sir. In time. In the last month I have learned to handle division. I can determine, and correctly, integral quotients and decimal quotients."

"Decimal quotients? To how many places?"

Programmer Shuman tried to keep his tone casual. "Any number!"

Loesser's lower jaw dropped. "Without a computer?"

"Set me a problem."

"Divide twenty-seven by thirteen. Take it to six places."

Five minutes later, Shuman said, "Two point oh seven six nine two three."

Loesser checked it. "Well, now, that's amazing. Multiplication didn't impress me too much because it involved integers after all, and I thought trick manipulation might do it. But decimals—"

"And that is not all. There is a new development that is, so far, top secret and which, strictly speaking, I ought not to mention. Still—— We may have made a break-through on the square root front."

"Square roots?"

"It involves some tricky points and we haven't licked the bugs yet, but Technician Aub, the man who invented the science and who has an amazing intuition in connection with it, maintains he has the problem almost solved. And he is only a Technician. A man like yourself, a trained and talented mathematician ought to have no difficulty."

"Square roots," muttered Loesser, attracted.

"Cube roots, too. Are you with us?"

Loesser's hand thrust out suddenly, "Count me in."

General Weider stumped his way back and forth at the head of the room and addressed his listeners after the fashion of a savage teacher facing a group of recalcitrant students. It made no difference to the general that they were the civilian scientists heading Project Number. The general was the over-all head, and he so considered himself at every waking moment.

He said, "Now square roots are all fine. I can't do them myself and I don't understand the methods, but they're fine. Still, the Project will not be sidetracked into what some of you call the fundamentals. You can play with graphitics any way you want to after the war is over, but right now we have specific and very practical problems to solve."

In a far corner, Technician Aub listened with painful attention. He was no longer a Technician, of course, having been relieved of his duties and assigned to the Project, with a fine-sounding title and good pay. But, of course, the social distinction remained and the highly placed scientific leaders could never bring themselves to admit him to their ranks on a footing of equality. Nor, to do Aub justice, did he, himself, wish it. He was as uncomfortable with them as they with him.

The general was saying, "Our goal is a simple one, gentlemen; the replacement of the computer. A ship that can navigate space without a computer on board can be constructed in one fifth the time and at one tenth the expense of a computer-laden ship. We could build fleets five times, ten times, as great as Deneb could if we could but eliminate the computer.

"And I see something even beyond this. It may be fantastic now; a mere dream; but in the future I see the manned missile!"

There was an instant murmur from the audience.

The general drove on. "At the present time, our chief bottleneck is the fact that missiles are limited in intelligence. The computer controlling them can only be so large, and for that reason they can meet the changing nature of anti-missile defenses in an unsatisfactory way. Few missiles, if any, accomplish their goal and missile warfare is coming to a dead end; for the enemy, fortunately, as well as for ourselves.

"On the other hand, a missile with a man or two within, controlling flight by graphitics, would be lighter, more mobile, more intelligent. It would give us a lead that might well mean the margin of victory. Besides which, gentlemen, the exigencies of war compel us to remember one thing. A man is much more dispensable than a computer. Manned missiles could be launched in numbers and under circumstances that no good general would care to undertake as far as computer-directed missilies are concerned——"

He said much more but Technician Aub did not wait.

Technician Aub, in the privacy of his quarters, labored long over the note he was leaving behind. It read finally as follows:

"When I began the study of what is now called graphitics, it was no more than a hobby. I saw no more in it than an interesting amusement, an exercise of mind.

"When Project Number began, I thought that others were wiser than I; that graphitics might be put to practical use as a benefit to mankind, to aid in the production of really practical mass-transference devices perhaps. But now I see it is to be used only for death and destruction.

"I cannot face the responsibility involved in having invented graphitics."

He then deliberately turned the focus of a protein-depolarizer on himself and fell instantly and painlessly dead.

They stood over the grave of the little Technician while tribute was paid to the greatness of his discovery.

Programmer Shuman bowed his head along with the rest of them, but remained unmoved. The Technician had done his share and was no longer needed, after all. He might have started graphitics, but now that it had started, it would carry on by itself overwhelmingly, triumphantly, until manned missiles were possible with who knew what else.

Nine times seven, thought Shuman with deep satisfaction, is sixty-three, and I don't need a computer to tell me so. The computer is in my own head.

And it was amazing the feeling of power that gave him.

About the author

Isaac Asimov (1920–   ) combines the career of scientist with that of writer. He is a professor of biochemistry at Boston University's medical school, as well as one of today's leading writers of science fiction. His interest in this type of literature developed at an early age. Later, he was able to pay his way through Columbia University on the proceeds from his own science fiction writings. He has written more than forty books, half of which are science books for the layman, and the rest science fiction.

Questions for discussion

1. Why did the Technician, Aub, kill himself? In what way were his feelings similar to the feelings of some of the nuclear physicists of our times?

2. In learning to depend upon computers, what present-day skills and knowledge have the people of this story forgotten?

3. Any good science fiction story is based upon certain assumptions as to what is going to happen during the next few centuries. What are the assumptions in this story?

4. This story is a *satire*. A satire is a narrative in which certain kinds of human behavior and attitudes are ridiculed through the use of exaggeration. Among the people of our society who are satirized here are the scientists. What other groups in our society are satirized? Which of their characteristics are satirized through exaggeration?

5. What general failings of the human race are satirized in this story?

6. What advantages does the Congressman see if Project Number is successful? What advantages does the General see?

7. What is the main interest for the reader in this story? Is it in the action, the character, or the theme? Support your answer.

8. Part of the fun of this story lies in the upside-down view the characters have of our own society. For example, "The cave men with their *triremes, stone axes and railroads* had no computers." Find other examples in the latter half of the story.

9. Part of the fun of the story lies in the strange view the reader gets of life in the future. For example, ". . . in theory there is nothing the computer can do that the human mind can't do." Find other examples. What, for example, is the General's ultimate goal? What seems to be the greatest intellectual triumph that Loesser, the mathematician, looks forward to? What gives the Programmer, Shuman, a "feeling of power"?

10. Do you think you can do a better job of explaining how to multiply seventeen times twenty-three than Aub did? Try an oral explanation for the class.

Vocabulary growth

CONTEXT. Reread the context of the following sentences on the pages indicated, and work out a meaning for each italicized word. Check your estimate of these words with the dictionary.

  a. Page 152, "He smoked Denebian tobacco with the air of one whose patriotism was so *notorious*, he could be allowed such liberties."
  b. Page 156, ". . . the congressman rose and his deep voice auto-

matically took on some of the *cadences* he used in public debate."
c. Page 157, "As the human brain takes over, more of our energy can be directed into peacetime *pursuits* and the *impingement* of war on the ordinary man will be less."
d. Page 158, "Communications devices become less *massive* and more efficient constantly."

For composition

1. How is your imagination working? Write a statement of what life will be like 100 years from now. What will people have learned? What will they have forgotten?
2. The writer seems to say that there will always be war. Do you agree? Disagree? Write a defense of your opinion giving facts and reasons.
3. Go to the library and find what material you can on one of the following subjects. Then write a report upon it.

   a. Hydroponics   c. Machines That Learn
   b. New Uses for Computers   d. Machines That Make Machines

The Parsley Garden

WILLIAM SAROYAN

When a boy is humiliated, he wants to get even. There are many ways to get even as you will discover.

ONE day in August Al Condraj was wandering through Woolworth's without a penny to spend when he saw a small hammer that was not a toy but a real hammer and he was possessed with a longing to have it. He believed it was just what he needed by which to break the monotony and with which to make something. He had gathered some first-class nails from Foley's Packing House where the boxmakers worked and where they had carelessly dropped at least fifteen cents' worth. He had gladly gone to the trouble of gathering them together because it had seemed to him that a nail, as such, was not something to be wasted. He had the nails, perhaps a half pound of them, at least two hundred of them, in a paper bag in the apple box in which he kept his junk at home.

Now, with the ten-cent hammer he believed he could make something out of box wood and the nails, although he had no idea what. Some sort of a table perhaps, or a small bench.

At any rate he took the hammer and slipped it into the pocket of his overalls, but just as he did so a man took him firmly by the arm without a word and pushed him to the back of the store into a small office. Another man, an older one, was seated behind a desk in the office, working with papers. The younger man, the one who had captured him, was excited and his forehead was covered with sweat.

"Well," he said, "here's one more of them."

The man behind the desk got to his feet and looked Al Condraj up and down.

"What's *he* swiped?"

"A hammer." The young man looked at Al with hatred. "Hand it over," he said.

The boy brought the hammer out of his pocket and handed it to the young man, who said, "I ought to hit you over the head with it, that's what I ought to do."

He turned to the older man, the boss, the manager of the store, and he said, "What do you want me to do with him?"

"Leave him with me," the older man said.

The younger man stepped out of the office, and the older man sat down and went back to work. Al Condraj stood in the office fifteen minutes before the older man looked at him again.

"Well," he said.

Al didn't know what to say. The man wasn't looking at him, he was looking at the door.

Finally Al said, "I didn't mean to steal it. I just need it and I haven't got any money."

"Just because you haven't got any money doesn't mean you've got a right to steal things," the man said. "Now, does it?"

"No, sir."

"Well, what am I going to do with you? Turn you over to the police?"

Al didn't say anything, but he certainly didn't want to be turned over to the police. He hated the man, but at the same time he realized somebody else could be a lot tougher than he was being.

"If I let you go, will you promise never to steal from this store again?"

"Yes, sir."

"All right," the man said. "Go out this way and don't come back to this store until you've got some money to spend."

He opened a door to the hall that led to the alley, and Al Condraj hurried down the hall and out into the alley.

The first thing he did when he was free was laugh, but he knew he had been humiliated, and he was deeply ashamed. It was not in his nature to take things that did not belong to him. He hated the young man who had caught him and he hated the manager of the store who had made him stand in silence in the office so long. He hadn't liked it at all when the young man had said he ought to hit him over the head with the hammer.

He should have had the courage to look him straight in the eye and say, "You and who else?"

Of course he *had* stolen the hammer and he had been caught, but it seemed to him he oughtn't to have been so humiliated.

After he had walked three blocks he decided he didn't want to go home just yet, so he turned around and started walking back to town. He almost believed he meant to go back and say something to the young man who had caught him. And then he wasn't sure he didn't mean to go back and steal the hammer again, and this time *not* get caught. As long as he had been made to feel like a thief anyway, the least he ought to get out of it was the hammer.

Outside the store he lost his nerve, though. He stood in the street, looking in, for at least ten minutes.

Then, crushed and confused and now bitterly ashamed of himself, first for having stolen something, then for having been caught, then for having been humiliated, then for not having guts enough to go back and do the job right, he began walking home again, his mind so troubled that he didn't greet his pal Pete Wawchek when they came face to face outside Graf's Hardware.

When he got home he was too ashamed to go inside and examine his junk, so he had a long drink of water from the faucet in the back yard. The faucet was used by his mother to water the stuff she planted every year: okra, bell peppers, tomatoes, cucumbers, onions, garlic, mint, eggplants and parsley.

His mother called the whole business the parsley garden, and every night in the summer she would bring chairs out of the house and put them around the table she had had Ondro, the neighborhood handyman, make for her for fifteen cents, and she would sit at the table and enjoy the cool of the garden and the smell of the things she had planted and tended.

Sometimes she would even make a salad and moisten the flat old-country bread and slice some white cheese, and she and he would have supper in the parsley garden. After supper she would attach the water hose to the faucet and water her plants and the place would be cooler than ever and it would smell real good, real fresh and cool and green, all the different growing things making a green-garden smell out of themselves and the air and the water.

After the long drink of water he sat down where the parsley itself was growing and he pulled a handful of it out and slowly ate it.

Then he went inside and told his mother what had happened. He even told her what he had *thought* of doing after he had been turned loose: to go back and steal the hammer again.

"I don't want you to steal," his mother said in broken English. "Here is ten cents. You go back to that man and you give him this money and you bring it home, that hammer."

"No," Al Condraj said. "I won't take your money for something I don't really need. I just thought I ought to have a hammer, so I could make something if I felt like it. I've got a lot of nails and some box wood, but I haven't got a hammer."

"Go buy it, that hammer," his mother said.

"No," Al said.

"All right," his mother said. "Shut up."

That's what she always said when she didn't know what else to say.

Al went out and sat on the steps. His humiliation was beginning to really hurt now. He decided to wander off along the railroad tracks to Foley's because he needed to think about it some more. At Foley's he watched Johnny Gale nailing boxes for ten minutes, but Johnny was too busy to notice him or talk to him, although one day at Sunday school, two or three years ago, Johnny had greeted him and said, "How's the boy?" Johnny worked with a boxmaker's hatchet and everybody in Fresno said he was the fastest boxmaker in town. He was the closest thing to a machine any packing house ever saw. Foley himself was proud of Johnny Gale.

Al Condraj finally set out for home because he didn't want to get in the way. He didn't want somebody working hard to notice that he was being watched and maybe say to him, "Go on, beat it." He didn't want Johnny Gale to do something like that. He didn't want to invite another humiliation.

On the way home he looked for money but all he found was the usual pieces of broken glass and rusty nails, the things that were always cutting his bare feet every summer.

When he got home his mother had made a salad and set the table, so he sat down to eat, but when he put the food in his mouth he just didn't care for it. He got up and went into the three-room house and got his apple box out of the corner of his room and went through his junk. It was all there, the same as yesterday.

He wandered off back to town and stood in front of the closed store, hating the young man who had caught him, and then he went along to the Hippodrome and looked at the display photographs from the two movies that were being shown that day.

Then he went along to the public library to have a look at all the books again, but he didn't like any of them, so he wandered around town some more, and then around half-past eight he went home and went to bed.

His mother had already gone to bed because she had to be up at five to go to work at Inderrieden's, packing figs. Some days there would be work all day, some days there would be only half a day of it, but whatever his mother earned during the summer had to keep them the whole year.

He didn't sleep much that night because he couldn't get over what had happened, and he went over six or seven ways by which to adjust the matter. He went so far as to believe it would be necessary to kill the young man who had caught him. He also believed it would be necessary for him to steal systematically and successfully the rest of his life. It was a hot night and he couldn't sleep.

Finally, his mother got up and walked barefooted to the kitchen for a drink of water and on the way back she said to him softly, "Shut up."

When she got up at five in the morning he was out of the house, but that had happened many times before. He was a restless boy, and he kept moving all the time every summer. He was making mistakes and paying for them, and he had just tried stealing and had been caught at it and he was troubled. She fixed her breakfast, packed her lunch and hurried off to work, hoping it would be a full day.

It was a full day, and then there was overtime, and although she had no more lunch she decided to work on for the extra money, anyway. Almost all the other packers were staying on, too, and her neighbor across the alley, Leeza Ahboot, who worked beside her, said, "Let us work until the work stops, then we'll go home and fix a supper between us and eat it in your parsley garden where it's so cool. It's a hot day and there's no sense not making an extra fifty or sixty cents."

When the two women reached the garden it was almost nine o'clock, but still daylight, and she saw her son nailing pieces of box wood together, making something with a hammer. It looked like a bench. He had already watered the garden and tidied up the rest of the yard, and the place seemed very nice, and her son seemed very serious and busy. She and Leeza went straight to work for their supper, picking bell peppers and tomatoes and cucumbers and a great deal of parsley for the salad.

Then Leeza went to her house for some bread which she had baked the night before, and some white cheese, and in a few minutes they were having supper together and talking pleasantly about the successful day they had had. After supper, they made Turkish coffee over an open fire in the yard. They drank the coffee and smoked a cigarette apiece, and told one another stories about their experiences in the old country and here in Fresno, and then they looked into their cups at the grounds to see if any good fortune was indicated, and there was: health and work and supper out of doors in the summer and enough money for the rest of the year.

Al Condraj worked and overheard some of the things they said, and then Leeza went home to go to bed, and his mother said, "Where you get it, that hammer, Al?"

"I got it at the store."

"How you get it? You steal it?"

Al Condraj finished the bench and sat on it. "No," he said. "I didn't steal it."

"How you get it?"

"I worked at the store for it," Al said.

"The store where you steal it yesterday?"

"Yes."

"Who give you job?"

"The boss."

"What you do?"

"I carried different stuff to the different counters."

"Well, that's good," the woman said. "How long you work for that little hammer?"

"I worked all day," Al said. "Mr. Clemmer gave me the hammer after I'd worked one hour, but I went right on working. The fellow who caught me yesterday showed me what to do, and we worked together. We didn't talk, but at the end of the day he took me to Mr. Clemmer's office and he told Mr. Clemmer that I'd worked hard all day and ought to be paid at least a dollar."

"That's good," the woman said.

"So Mr. Clemmer put a silver dollar on his desk for me, and then the fellow who caught me yesterday told him the store needed a boy like me every day, for a dollar a day, and Mr. Clemmer said I could have the job."

"That's good," the woman said. "You can make it a little money for yourself."

"I left the dollar on Mr. Clemmer's desk," Al Condraj said, "and I told them both I didn't want the job."

"Why you say that?" the woman said. "Dollar a day for eleven-year-old boy good money. Why you not take job?"

"Because I hate the both of them," the boy said. "I would never work for people like that. I just looked at them and picked up my hammer and walked out. I came home and I made this bench."

"All right," his mother said. "Shut up."

His mother went inside and went to bed, but Al Condraj sat on the bench he had made and smelled the parsley garden and didn't feel humiliated any more.

But nothing could stop him from hating the two men, even though he knew they hadn't done anything they shouldn't have done.

About the author

William Saroyan (1908–   ) was born into an Armenian family in California. The people in his family, and in the Armenian community in which he grew up are presented in his stories with pride, humor, and sympathy. But while he portrays the distinctive qualites of these Armenian folk, he also writes of the lives and problems of all men. Saroyan began writing at the age of thirteen, and poured out quantities of materials before winning publication. His short story, "The Daring Young Man on the Flying Trapeze" brought him fame in 1934. His short stories and novels, particularly *The Human Comedy*, have won him a place in the front rank of American writers. He has written several short plays and full-length dramas. *The Time of Your Life* won the Pulitzer Prize in 1940.

Questions for discussion

1. Why did Al refuse the dollar and the job that Mr. Clemmer offered him? What is your opinion of this refusal?
2. How did Mr. Clemmer feel about Al when he was caught stealing?

What did the young man think of Al at this time? What did the men think of Al at the close of the story? Which of the two men had changed his opinion of Al?

3. What was Al's feeling toward the men after he had been caught? Why did he hate Mr. Clemmer who had let him go? What did Mr. Clemmer do that humiliated Al?

4. What was Al's feeling toward these two men at the close of the story? Why do you suppose he still felt this way? Was this feeling just and reasonable?

5. Why did Al refuse the money his mother offered him?

6. The author emphasizes over and over again that Al felt humiliated. That is, his pride had been hurt. Why did Al feel ashamed? You will find the answer in a paragraph on page 166.

7. What possible courses of action did Al consider as "ways by which to adjust the matter"? Were you surprised that he decided to work for the hammer? It must have hurt his pride to have to go back and ask the man for a job. Why did he do so? Was it because he wanted the hammer so much?

8. What kind of a person was Al's mother? Why do you suppose that she did not insist that Al go back and take the job? Was money important to her? What else was more important to her than money?

9. Why is the story entitled "The Parsley Garden"? Look back at the paragraphs in which the garden is mentioned. What does the parsley garden do for Leeza and Al's mother? What effect does it have on Al himself?

10. This is a story about an eleven-year-old boy, but the author hopes to make the reader see himself in the boy's thoughts and actions. He stands for all of us. The loss of self-respect and its recovery are experiences that all of us have had. What is the main idea, or theme of this story?

Vocabulary growth

WORDS ARE INTERESTING. If you look in the dictionary, you will see that *humble, humility,* and *humiliate* all come from a Latin word meaning "low," akin to *humus,* or earth. What connection do you see between "earth" and the meaning of *humiliate:* "to lower the pride or dignity of"?

WORD FORMATION. Thousands of English words are built up by the addition of suffixes to base words. For example, in the story above, the words *systematically* and *successfully* appear. You can see the base words *system* and *success.* You can also see the suffixes *-atic, -al, -ly,* and

-ful. How many words can you build on the following base words. You may add prefixes too.

act   add   fix
form   time   grade

For composition

1. For Al and his mother, the parsley garden was a refuge, a place of calm and peace where the problems of living could be looked at quietly. Do you have such a refuge? Describe it in terms of what it does for you.

2. What happens when you get caught doing something wrong? Did you hate those who caught you? Did you plan to "get even"? Did you "get even"? Write a short narrative describing the experience and your reaction to it.

3. It has often been said that the way to gain an enemy is to do a favor. Conversely, it often appears that you like a person whom you have helped in some way. Do these observations check with your experience? Write your own opinion, supported by instances from your experience.

Fishermen

JOHAN BOJER

It began when the father felt a pain in his back. The pain and illness grew bringing perplexing questions to the four sons. What could they do? Was their decision the right one?

I

THE little islands of the fishing station, lying under dark winter skies, were scattered like swimming birds on the surface of the sea, surrounded by driving snow and the grey, rolling ocean. Out of the little buildings among the rocks smoke curled up, and from the narrow channels between the islets rose a growing sound as in the twilight one boat after the other returned from the banks with their fish. They unloaded their catch on the rocks, or landed at some quay in order to sell, or even circled round the trading-vessels riding at anchor in the wide bay. New boats came in from the high sea, their rigging heavy with ice, with a crowd of gulls and divers in the air above them, fighting against the wind and screaming shrilly.

When the newcomers were near enough for their crews to be seen, the men looked like fantastic supernatural beings, for the spray from the waves and the snow from the air had frozen on their oilskins, their eyebrows and beards.

On the islet farthest out towards the sea there was one solitary building, like a guard against the rolling ocean. After darkness set in, a boat landed there, and began at once to take ashore the day's catch. The owner was Andreas Skaret. Like many of the fishermen at the station, he was a small farmer from the inner fiords, seeking half his living by bank fishing in winter: and since his four sons were grown up, he could man his own boat, keep his own building at the station, and even as a rule choose his own route over the hidden banks under the sea.

When the fish lay on the rocks, the five men waded heavily ashore, stopping to beat their hands against their sides in order to get warm. Their oilskins were frozen stiff, and made a great noise as they moved. Going indoors or eating was not to be thought of, although they had not tasted food since the morning. The catch had to be looked after first; it could not be allowed to freeze while still containing the liver.

The wind drove sleet and salt spray over them, but the five fishermen turned their backs upon it, their knives working and the fish blood running freely. Each of them was provided with a lantern from which a yellow glare fell on the slippery rocks. The sea kept up its roaring song, and a few yards away white tongues of foam surged up, only to sink back in darkness, hissing.

Not a word was spoken. About midnight, however, the old man cried loudly enough to be heard in the storm:

"You'd better go in and prepare something hot, Karl."

A little later he himself sheathed his gory knife and walked slowly into the little shack. In there he remained standing, holding his cold hands above the stove, the layers of ice on his wrist melting, so that fish, blood, and slime dripped on the hot stove, hissing as they fell. Soon, also, his big brown beard began to drip, countless little icicles thawing slowly. It took time, however, before the sea boots were sufficiently thawed to be turned down and pulled off. The stockings were frozen, and not till they also had been changed and he could slip his feet into dry wooden clogs did he ask his son:

"Is supper ready? It would feel good to eat something hot." With a weary gesture he stroked his furrowed forehead, yawning. Then he seemed to break down, sitting, elbows on knees, staring at the fire.

The door opened, and the three other sons entered noisily. The cold winter air came in through the door before them like white smoke, and their frozen kits spread cold about the small room.

The youngest poured a panful of steaming hot fish soup into a tin dish on the table, then placed potatoes and boiled fish beside it. There was so little space, and the floor was so filled up with chests and various things, that they had to step carefully to reach their seats.

When finally seated about the smoking fish-oil lamp, they were too tired to speak. They simply fed. Once only the father lifted his weather-sore eyes from the dish to ask:

"Did you fasten the boat properly? We may have a storm to-night."

The three elder sons continued their meal for some time before mumbling, "H-m," which was meant for "Yes."

Forty years of fishing life had turned the old man's face into the semblance of dark and deeply furrowed bark. His shoulders stooped, but he fed with a purposeful tenacity, which made him perspire freely. The two older sons were rather small and thick-set, like their father; the two younger ones, tall, fair giants. Their swollen hands shone red every time they dipped their spoons into the fish, and fish blood and slime had been barely wiped off on their trousers, so that much stuck yet, especially around their nails.

The meal finished, the young men lit their pipes and went to bed, after hanging up all their wet kit. The beds were wooden bunks, nailed to the wall one above the other. Once in bed, the sons went on smoking. Their father remained astride a chest, with his back close by the stove, as if he was not yet fully warm.

Finally he, too, went to bed. The lamp was put out. The stove was still hot, and the wet sea kits reeked of sea, sweat and fish slime. A few hours later, however, the peat was burned out, and the icy night air crept in through abundant cracks in the wooden walls. The clothes, which had until then kept dripping, stiffened, and were covered with white hoarfrost.

The four brothers snored apace, dead-tired, and carrying on their heavy work even in their dreams. They were riding on high-crested waves, they were hauling nets, they cried out loudly, and perhaps once in a while they had a glimpse of an old woman at the little farm on the fiord waiting for her five men to return in spring.

When next morning they made ready to put to sea, the old man remained sitting in full sea kit, pressing one hand to his back.

Two sons were already on the beach near the boat; the third threw a net over his shoulders as he went out. The father made as if to rise, and sat down again.

"Are you ill, Father?" asked the son who was still with him.

His father stroked his forehead.

"I have not felt warm all night. The frost is inside, like. And I have a sharp pain in my back just here."

"Have a few drops of ether; perhaps it will ease you."

The old man rose up for something or other, only to tumble in a heap on a chest.

"Nay, Father, you'd better stay ashore today." The son helped him into his bed and covered him up well. Then he gave him ether, filled the stove with peat, and left. A few minutes later the boat steered seaward.

In the twilight the men returned with a good catch. As usual, their first thought was to open the fish, which must not freeze while containing liver. They were one less this time; it would take longer.

When the fish were ashore, the youngest ran up at once in his heavy seaboots to see how his father fared.

The room was icy cold. In the dark bunk the old man lay huddled up under his sheepskin rug. His head was strangely red; beads of perspiration stood on his forehead.

"Father, how do you feel?"

The old man turned over. His eyes were hot. He shook his head faintly, and pulled his sheepskins well up again.

The son went down on the rocks where the others were at work. His eldest brother called out to him to hurry up about it. An hour later he cried out once more:

"No chance of father lending a hand?"

"No," replied the other, and no more was said.

II

It was well after midnight when the youngest brother was allowed to go up and prepare food. When he offered hot soup to his father, the old man turned his head away. He did not want anything.

The others entered, making a great deal of noise while undressing among chests and boxes. The sick man writhed. It hurt his aching head, but it did not occur to him for a moment to ask them to be more quiet.

After the meal the eldest son asked:

"Are you ill, Father?"

After a while the answer came from the bed—— "H-m," which meant that he felt very ill indeed.

The four younger men charged their pipes, filling the small space with choking smoke. Their father coughed but said nothing.

When they were about to go to bed, he at last answered:

"You will have to find me some turpentine. This pain in my back won't stop."

"I hope it is not going to be pneumonia," said the youngest son, softly. The others, who were sitting on their beds took their pipes out of their mouths, looking towards the old man with serious faces.

When the eldest son had finished his pipe, he produced a bottle from his chest, and rummaged until he found a woolen glove, which he soaked with turpentine.

"Where is the pain?" he asked.

The old man sighed, stirring slightly.

"Oh, it keeps moving, but try here," pointing to his left side.

He was still fully dressed. The younger man unbuttoned his clothes and placed the turpentine poultice on his father's broad hairy chest. The patient groaned.

"I don't think it would be a bad thing if you swallowed a little turpentine, either," the youngest son remarked.

"Oh, yes, I've heard that is a good thing against pangs," said the third son, moving into his bed and emitting more smoke than ever.

Without waiting for his father to reply, the eldest son filled a small glass half full of turpentine, dropped an uncertain number of drops of ether into it, and bent over the bed.

"Here, Father."

The old man hardly knew what he was doing. He turned his face up and let the other pour the contents of the glass into his mouth. A few drops went down the wrong way, and he coughed a good deal afterward.

Then they all went to bed, the small building shivering in the storm, the sea roaring, and the tiny window slowly turning white with icy crystals.

When next morning the youngest son went to his father's bed with a cup of coffee, he thought for a moment that the old man was well again, because he was talking and laughing to himself.

A few minutes afterward, however, he bent over his eldest brother.

"You'll have to get up, Isak," he said softly. "Father is in a bad way, I'm afraid."

They gave up the trip to sea for that day, sitting each on his seachest, smoking, saying next to nothing. They understood that their father was seriously ill, and they did not know what in the world to do about it. Now and then one of them would look out of the window. The fishing-vessels were returning. Perhaps some of them were quite full today. In order to avoid wasting time altogether, they started mending nets, which they brought into the shack from the shed on the beach. Later in the day the sick man had a slight hemorrhage. After that no word was said. The mending needles went in and out in unbroken silence.

Toward evening the second son said hoarsely:

"Perhaps we ought to sail for the doctor." It was over twenty miles sailing to the mainland, where the nearest doctor lived.

Half an hour later the eldest brother threaded a fresh needle and then said:

"If it is pneumonia, he'll stay in bed for weeks."

"H-m," the others said, looking up for a moment.

"And somebody must look after him night and day."

"H-m."

"But sea fishing for three men is impossible, and it is not easy to find a hired man."

"H-m." They all agreed to that.

Finally the eldest brother rose to look out of the window.

"Perhaps the best thing would be to take father on board and sail him home to mother."

"H-m—yes." They looked straight before them for a moment.

"And then perhaps we might find a hired man, and return here to finish the season."

"H-m."

The old man grew worse towards evening, and the next morning their resolve was taken despite uncertain weather. The bedclothes fluttered before the wind while they carried them to the boat. There was no cabin, and they had to make a bed in the open stern-sheets. First they spread straw underneath, then a sheepskin rug and a pillow at the stern. In the room they thought for a moment of nailing some boards together for a stretcher, but the third son said in a most flippant tone of voice:

"Oh, I think I shall manage him myself." They dressed their father in his best kit. Only they could not get his seaboots on him, because he was unable to lend any help of his own. He hardly knew what they were doing with him, babbling like a drunken man all the time.

III

Finally, the slow little procession marched down the rocky path towards the boat. First came the eldest brother with a chest of provisions, then the third, treading softly on the slippery rocks, nursing his father in his arms as if he were a baby. The other two came last, each carrying a bundle of fresh fish for mother.

The boat lay stern shoreward, but it lay deep in the water, and the third son had to put his father down on the rocks in order to pull his sea-boots up high enough. Then once more lifting the old man, he waded carefully out, feeling his way every moment, so as to avoid a false step. At last the sick man was lying in his swaying bed.

They covered him up to the eyes with sheepskin rugs, and his head was covered with a huge fur cap, so that nothing of his face could be seen. Sailing out of the sound, however, a drop of salt water struck the cap, instantly freezing to ice.

The old man was still babbling. He fancied he was at home, and scolded his wife because dinner was not ready.

The broad squaresail was hoisted, and swelled before the wind; the boat heeled over, picking out her course to the mainland. The eldest brother held the tiller, the youngest looked after the sheet-ropes, and before the mast the other two watched the tack, for the east wind came sidewise.

The grey sea rolled in long, heavy billows; the wind sang in sail and rigging. It was in the middle of February; a bare, blue, frosty sky stretched above the endless grey sea. Soon the fishing station was on the horizon like a string of blurred points.

From the moment when the eldest brother took the tiller, it was out of the question in this weather to ask behind him how his father fared. The captain in a boat has to look after the sail, feel all the little outside purposes of the boat, and see to it that every man on board does his duty, and at the same time he must watch every wave of any size coming up, estimate its force, its direction, and its bearing on the boat. Isak was famed for having inherited his father's ability for sailing, and today his task was twofold. He had to press the boat in order to get forward as quickly as possible, and at the same time he had to avoid shipping too much water, to keep the old man dry. Also, a captain without a compass must all the while keep listening to his secret instinct whispering which course to steer.

The wind grew; and monstrous white-crested waves came rolling out of the east, foaming and roaring. But at the very moment when each wave was ready to break over the tiny vessel, she pointed her nose aslant uphill and flew upward; then she rode a little way on the foaming crest before dipping her nose once more towards the deep hollow between one wave and the next; only to ride on the back of it in a few more moments. It was a game played between the sea and the tiller; each separate wave threatening to swallow the boat had to be cheated of its purpose. The little vessel at such times becomes part and parcel of her captain's body and soul, or rigging, tiller, and boat grow to be a strange instrument for his skilled fingers to play upon. If it proved impossible to avoid shipping some water, Isak shipped it forward, and the youngest of them worked wonders bailing. Both men forward were already so covered with frozen spray that they looked like Arctic sea-monsters.

Far away, westward, they could barely see some hidden rocks causing the sea to spout foam skyward. To the east a yellow strip of wind-laden clouds lay low on the horizon, mirroring their light so that some waves rose golden, others rolled pitch-dark, but most were grey, with foaming crests.

The eldest brother's face was absolutely impassive where he stood, throwing the tiller from side to side above his sou'wester. The roar of the sea and the thin scream of the rigging drowned all other sounds. A couple of lonely gulls followed them, circling over the boat, crying forlornly. The boat held her landward course with her precious load.

The clouds thickened in the east; the wind grew. In a little while the captain had to call out, "Take in a reef." "Take in a reef," the youngest brother yelled, dropping his bailing-scoop. "Take in a reef," was heard from the fore-hold, when both men threw themselves on the sail to haul it down, while the youngest brother let out the halyard.

They went on under reduced canvas. About midday the sky was quite clouded, and snow began to drive before the storm. At last the blizzard shut them in till they could barely see two boat-lengths in any direction. The storm grew worse, and they had to take in another reef. There was no time even to think of their father any more.

With the sail half-way up, the small boat flew on like a frightened bird. The bailing-scoop in the hand of the youngest brother was a clumsy tool now, being a shapeless lump of ice. Everything turned to ice—gloves, boots, sou'westers, beards.

Hour after hour passed in this manner. The two gulls gave up and returned to the fishing-station. Because the blinding snow-drift prevented the captain from seeing clearly, he was taken unawares several times, a wave thundering in over the boat like a waterfall. Everything on board was afloat. The youngest brother no longer heeded the weight of his scoop; he was bailing, bailing. Even if his father were washed out of the boat now, he would have to keep bailing without stop. They ought to sight the lighthouse by now. The captain often stole a glance sideward, but he could see nothing. The storm was now so heavy that the last reef was taken. With less canvas, the boat would lose her steering-way, and she needed speed to ride over the waves.

The sail grew heavy with spray. The mast had no ropes any more, only cables of ice. The heavy rigging pressed her still more under, and they shipped more water.

Hours passed, and the lighthouse did not appear. It was a lucky thing that no one could see how pale the captain was growing. At last twilight set in, and suddenly the youngest brother screamed:

"Where are we? Have you seen the lighthouse?"

The captain made believe not to hear.

"Keep bailing!" he roared. And the youngest man was wont to obey.

All of them knew that in a blizzard the wind often turns without the sailors perceiving it. The boat deviates from her original course by slow degrees, the captain relying upon the sail, being unable to see anything but sea and drifting snow. If now the wind had changed to south, they were heading straight out across the Arctic Ocean.

Darkness fell, the small boat plunged more and more heavily. Suddenly the captain felt a hand on his arm. He looked behind him and saw his father crawling out of the bed clothes, holding on to the rail to avoid being flung overboard.

"No, no, Father! Lie down!" the son yelled.

"No, no; this is bad. We have the wind from the north. I feel this is all wrong. Board tack [1] and steer straight before the wind."

Before they could realize what had happened, the old man was in

---

[1] **Board tack:** The sails were set so that the wind drove straight into them and the boat drove straight ahead with wind and waves behind it.

the hold without his sea-boots. At that same moment the boat was under a wave, threatening to capsize. There was no time to ask how their father felt, ill or well. No time to think of his health. He seized the tiller, taking his usual place in the boat, and the eldest son turned off to help his brother bailing.

"Board tack!" With their ingrained obedience, they carried out the order. The boat lifted herself, turned her nose and flew before both wind and waves. For long spaces of time she rode on the tall crests of the waves with a speed to make the sail hang slack against the mast.

The old man had no longer pneumonia, no longer fever. His whole being was bent on the one purpose of saving their lives and their boat.

A tremendous thing, this, to let go before the weather. It means for the fisherman to throw dice with fate itself. Perhaps he steers homeward, perhaps out to sea, straight to perdition. He believes the wind comes from the north, but it may be that it comes from the south. The next moment he may strike a hidden rock and be lost. It is not impossible that he heads straight for the shore somewhere. Nobody knows for certain. In his thoughts the sailor says, "O Lord God!" sailing on. But he does not know where.

Both brothers were bailing, bailing, but it became a more and more difficult task to keep the boat empty.

The old man was soon grey with ice, like the others. If he was feverish, the waves dashing over his head from behind would certainly cool him. Suddenly they saw him let go of the tiller; blood spouted from his mouth, and he tumbled down in the hold.

There was no time to give him any help. The eldest had to catch the tiller before the waves upset the boat, and soon the old man was drenched among the floating floorboards.

The waves shot them forward with a mad speed, tossing the boat like a ball in the darkness. The sea was so heavy that she steered only with great difficulty. And where were they going?

Suddenly there was a loud report. The sail tumbled down, covering the two in the fore-hold, and the mast fell. The frost had made the wood brittle, and now it was broken.

For a moment the boat remained still riding on a crest, then she turned, offering her broadside to the next wave, which broke over her in all its strength. Then a still greater wave lifted her high up, threw her before it into an abyss, and the next moment she disappeared.

When she appeared again, keel upward, four men hung on to the lower rigging. One after the other they climbed on to the upturned boat, clinging to the keel. All sou'westers were gone; their wet hair fluttered stiffly.

The boat tossed on. It was difficult to keep their hold. Otherwise, like all fishermen who are wrecked, they were perfectly calm. They knew what they had to do. As if at a signal, all four yelled their loudest, making a call for help that would carry far away. One wave drove the youngest off, but he caught hold of a rope and climbed up again.

Suddenly the eldest cried out, "Father!" and the others repeated heartbrokenly, "Father!"

"There!" the eldest cried, pointing. They saw something being lifted by a wave. In the same instant the second brother placed his foot on the keel, and, stretching his arms forward, leaped into the waves, disappearing under a breaking crest. The others had no leisure to look for him. They clung for life.

"Father!" they heard suddenly out of the darkness, and they saw their brother once more. He was treading water, holding something in his arms. A wave lifted him till they saw him against the sky, saw their father in his arms, and saw his desperate efforts to reach him.

"Father!" cried the three on the upturned boat. "Father!" came the reply out of the darkness. But then a wave broke over the swimmer; he sank down in the hollow; a fresh wave came, and he disappeared.

Late at night the sea threw the three ashore somewhere. They saw the lights from a house near by, but when they felt hard ground under them, they were too far spent to walk. They crawled on all fours across the snow up to the house. They had come ashore on Hitra, one of the outlying islands off the coast, but of considerable size.

In one or two days they were out of bed again. Their boat was found, not in a bad condition after all. They mended it, bought new rigging, and sailed home to mother with their sad news.

But after staying at home for a week or so they found two men for hire, and sailed back to Lofoten to finish the season's fishing.

Early in spring a man on Hitra, carting seaweed from the beach, found the corpses of two fishermen in sailing kit. The older man had no boots, and was clasped like a big doll in the arms of the younger. Both bodies were encased in a block of sea-green ice. The man unloaded his seaweed and went nearer, but he had literally to cut the two apart with his spade in order to place them safely on his sledge.

About the author

Johan Bojer (1872–1959) spent his early years in a fisherman's hut within sight of the sea and rocky beaches of the Norwegian coast. At an early age he decided to be a writer and pursued this goal by gathering experience in many of the capitals of Europe. Working in Paris as a correspondent for a Norwegian newspaper, Bojer met many of the leading writers of his time. His novels and short stories describe the lives of plain Norwegian people. Some of these stories are deep psychological studies of his characters; others are pictures of youth and outdoor life in Norway. The novel which won him great fame in this country was *The Great Hunger*.

Questions for discussion

1. The brothers "understood that their father was seriously ill, and they did not know what in the world to do about it."
   a. What did they do the first day?
   b. Why did they remain on shore the second day?
   c. Why did they decide not to go for the doctor?
2. What details show that the brothers were rough, crude men?
3. What details given on page 176 show a lack of consideration on the part of the sons for the comfort of the father? Did the brothers act this way because they had no love for their father or because they were crude and thoughtless men? What other details in the story do show their consideration for their father?
4. Were any of the brothers less concerned about their father than the others?
   a. Which brother rushed to the hut to see how the old man felt?
   b. Which brother prepared the turpentine poultice?
   c. Which brother carried the father to the boat?
   d. Which brother jumped into the sea to rescue the father?
5. Did the men know that they were heading into a storm? If they had known of the storm, is it likely that they would have started home? Was their decision to take their father home a reasonable one? Would it have been easier for the father if the brothers had brought a doctor to him? If they had arrived home safely, would the father have been better off than at the fishing station?

6. At the end, the father was certain that the wind was from the north. Was he right?
7. In a tragedy the characters are defeated by outside forces that are too powerful for them, or by their own weakness and ignorance. In what way was this tragedy of the fishermen caused by their weakness and ignorance? Before answering this question, turn back to the quoted words in the first question above.

Vocabulary growth

WORDS ARE INTERESTING. The word *board*, as it was used in this story, means "the side of a ship." Thus, *to go overboard* for something means "to jump over the side of the ship into the sea." When someone says that a proposal or a project has gone "by the board," he means that it has been lost or given up completely.

VARIANT MEANINGS. Many words in common usage have special meanings in trades and occupations. The following words, used in this story, are of this kind. Look up the meaning they have in sailing.

bail	sou'wester	tack
tiller	reef	heel

For composition

1. You are the man who discovered the bodies of the missing fishermen. Write an account of your discovery using the details about the sea, the island, and the discovery itself as provided in the story.
2. The public prosecutor is investigating the death of the father. Someone in the community has charged that the brothers were guilty of gross negligence in the care of their father. You may take either side.
   a. Write an accusation of the brothers, supporting it by details.
   b. Write a defense of the brothers.

Spring Victory

JESSE STUART

Some people in distress just give up. Others cry for help. And others react as the family in this story did.

"I don't know what to do," Mom said. "We've just enough bread for three more days. We don't have much of anything else to eat with our bread. This is a terrible winter and your father down sick."

Mom sat on a hickory-split-bottomed chair. She put the bottom in the chair last spring. I went to the woods after the sap got up and peeled the green hickory bark from the small hickory sapling. Mom took a case knife and scraped the green from the slats of bark and wove them across the bottom of a chair that Pa wanted to throw away.

"If your father was only well," Mom said and looked at the blazing forestick. "I'll have to think of something. You children run along and play. Leave me alone to think."

Sophie and I crossed the floorless dog-trot between the two big log-pens of our house. We called this dog-trot the "entry." We kept our stovewood and firewood stacked in the entry. This was a place where the rain, snow and sleet couldn't touch the wood. It was easy to walk out of the kitchen and carry an arm load of the stovewood for the kitchen stove when Mom was getting a meal. It was easy for me to carry firewood from the big stack in the entry to the fireplace where Mom was looking into the fire and dreaming now.

"There's not any place for us to run and play," Sophie said. "The only place we have to run and play is in the entry. And the cold wind blows through here."

"You are right," I said. "But Mom wants us to get away from her for a little while. Mom is worried."

Sophie stood by the firewood pile. She put her small white hand

186

upon a big oak backlog that had part of the dead bark slipped from it. Sophie's long blond hair was lifted from her shoulders by a puff of wind. The cold wind brought tears to her eyes. Beyond the entry we saw the pine-tops upon the mountainside sagging with snow. We couldn't see any briar thickets on the high hill slopes. They were snowed under. The garden fence posts barely stuck out of the snow. Four paths led away from our house—one to the barn, one to the smokehouse, one to the well and one to the hollow back of our house where Mom and I hauled wood with our horse. The big logs that Fred pulled with a long chain around them made a path through the deep snow from the dark hollow under the pines to our wood-yard.

"This snow has been on the ground since last November," Sophie said. "That was 1917. Now it is January, 1918. You are ten years old and I am thirteen years old."

We stood in the entry by the woodpile and talked until we got cold, then Sophie opened the door and we walked into the room. We hurried to the big bright fire to warm our cold hands. Mom was staring into the fireplace with her eagle-gray eyes. She looked steadily toward the fire. She was holding James on her lap. Mary was sitting in a small rocking chair beside her. Pa turned over in bed and asked for water.

Mom got up from the rocking chair with James in her arms. She walked toward Pa's bed. Mom poured a glass of water from a pitcher that was on a stand at the head of Pa's bed.

"Do you feel any better, Mick?" Mom said.

"Nope, I don't, Sal," he said. "I feel weak as water. I'll tell you that flu is bad stuff. I got up too soon and took a back-set."

Pa took the glass of water and drank. Mom stood and watched him with James in her arms.

"Is the firewood holding out?" Pa asked as he handed Mom the empty glass.

"Yes, it is," Mom said. "We have plenty of wood."

"How about food for the family and for the livestock?"

"We're getting along all right," Mom said. "Don't worry, Mick. We'll take care of everything. You get well just as soon as you can. You won't get well if you keep on worrying."

"I can't keep from worrying," Pa said. "Here I'm down sick and can't get out of bed. Crops failed us last year and we don't have bread for the children. And I've never seen such snow on the ground. This is a dark winter to me."

"It's a dark winter for all of us," Mom said. "But remember the snow will leave the hills one of these days and the sun will shine on blue violets under the last year's leaves."

Mom put the water glass back on the standtable beside the water pitcher. She walked back to her rocking chair. The firelight glowed over the room and tiny shadows flickered on the newspaper-papered walls.

"Son, we are not whipped yet," Mom said to me. "Your Pa is asleep now. I'll tell you what we are going to do."

I walked over beside Mom's chair. Sophie stood beside her too.

"Sophie can do the cooking," Mom said. "Can't you bake bread and cook potatoes, Sophie?"

"Yes, Mom."

"And you can use an ax well for a boy ten years old," Mom said.

"It's easy for me to chop with my pole-ax."

"Then you take your ax and go to the hills," Mom said, pointing from the front window to the steep snow-covered bluff east of our house. "You can find all kinds of tough-butted white oaks on the bluff over there. Cut them down, trim them and scoot them over the hill. We're going to make baskets out of them."

I kept my pole-ax in the entry by the firewood pile, where it would not be snowed under. As I walked out of the front room I pulled my toboggan cap low over my ears. I wrapped my overalls close around my legs so the snow wouldn't get around my feet. I picked up my pole-ax and walked down the path toward the barn. The cold whistling January wind stung my face. Fred nickered to me as I passed the barn. The creek was frozen over and the snow had covered the ice save for a hole that I had chopped so the cow and horse could get water.

I passed the water-hole and the empty hog pen. I started up the steep bluff toward the white-oak trees. The snow came to my waist. I held to bushes and pulled up the hills—breaking a tiny path through the waist-deep snow. Finally, I reached the white-oak grove and stood beneath a shaggy-topped white-oak sapling. The dead last year's leaves were still clinging to its boughs. These clusters of dead leaves were weighted with snow. When the sharp bit of my pole-ax hit the frozen white-oak wood, a loud ring struck the distant frozen hill across the valley. The sounds came back to my ears. Snow rained on me from the top of the white-oak sapling. I felled the white oak down the bluff toward the barn. I trimmed its branches and cut its top away. I slid the sapling over the bluff toward the barn. I cut twelve white-oak saplings, and trimmed and topped them and slid them over the bluff toward the barn.

It was easier for me to get down the bluff than it had been to climb it. The white-oak saplings had made a path through the deep snow. I followed this broken path toward the barn. I carried the white-oak saplings from the barn to the entry. I carried one at a time on my shoulder; the green, white-oak timber was heavy. After I'd carried them to the entry I went into the house to see what Mom wanted me to do next.

"After you warm yourself," Mom said, "I want you to take a handsaw and saw these white-oak saplings into six-foot lengths. After you saw them into lengths, I want you to split the lengths into four quarters and bring them to me."

By the time that Mom had given me instructions, I was warm enough to go to work again. I sawed the poles into six-foot lengths and split them with my pole-ax. I carried them into our front room and stacked them in a pile of small green fence rails. Mom looked the pile over and picked up one of the cuts and started to work. She used a butcher knife, a drawing knife and a case knife. She split the lengths again and again and ripped long splits from each length. She split one length into coarser splits to make ribs for the baskets. Another length she split into basket handles.

"I'm going to make feed baskets," Mom said. "People will always need feed baskets. I'm going to make them in three different sizes. I'm going to make peck baskets. Men will want peck baskets to carry eggs to town on Saturdays. They'll want them to carry salt, sugar and coffee from the store where they have a long way to walk. I'm going to make a half-bushel basket for it will be about the right size to carry corn to the mules, nubbins to the cows and ears of corn to the fattening hogs. And I'm going to make bushel feed baskets."

Sophie got supper that night and I fed Fred and fed and milked Gypsy. I found two more hens under our chicken-roost on the snow. They were frozen stiff as boards. I felt of their craws and I could feel only a few grains of corn. I didn't tell Mom about the chickens. I buried them in the snow. Every day a chicken, guinea or a turkey froze to death. Some days as many as six fowls would freeze to death. I found sparrows frozen to death around the barn. When I put hay down for Gypsy and gave her corn nubbins in a feed box I milked cold milk from her into the bucket. There was an icy stillness in the January night air and millions of bright stars shivered in a cold blue sky.

By the time that Sophie had steaming-hot corn bread baked, and I had done the feeding, the milking and carried in firewood and stovewood for the night, Mom had made two baskets. Sophie had crossed the entry from the kitchen to tell Mom that supper was ready, and I was putting my kindling wood in the corner to start the morning fire when Mom held up a basket to us.

"Look, children," she said. "I'm not quite as good as I used to be when I helped Pap make baskets. I need practice."

"Mom, that's a pretty basket," I said.

"Supper is ready," Sophie said.

We crossed the entry for supper. The starlight from the winter skies couldn't shine in at our entry. Mom carried a pine torch to light our way to the kitchen. Sophie led James across the entry and Mary held to Mom's skirt. The hot steaming corn bread was sweet to our taste. We had milk and bread and hot boiled potatoes.

"Tomorrow," Mom said, "I want you to saddle Fred and ride to Greenwood with four baskets. I'll have two more made by morning. Sell the peck basket for thirty-five cents. Sell the half-bushel basket for sixty cents. Sell the two bushel baskets for a dollar apiece. That will be two dollars and ninety-five cents if you sell all the baskets."

"I'll do it, Mom, just as soon as I get the feeding done," I said.

I went to bed that night and dreamed of riding Fred to town. I dreamed that my baskets sold. I dreamed that men wanted more baskets and I came home with my pockets filled with money and a load of corn meal, flour, lard and candy on Fred's back—all that he could carry.

I awoke and built a fire in the front room to warm it for Mom. She slept in a bed with Sophie and Mary just across from Pa's bed— in the other corner of the room. I slept upstairs with James. After I'd built the fire in the front room, I crossed the entry with a pine torch. It was yet before daylight on the short winter day. I put a fire in the stove and took my milk bucket and feed basket and started toward the barn. I fed Fred corn in his box and threw down hay from the loft. I forked hay to Gypsy's manger and gave her corn nubbins to eat while I milked her.

When I finished my work, Mom had cooked our breakfast. She made griddle cakes for us and we ate sorghum molasses with hot griddle cakes. After breakfast while Mom was feeding Pa, I put the saddle on Fred and bridled him. I rode to our front door. Mom came out with four baskets. She carried two in each hand.

"Watch old Fred," Mom said. "Do be careful. If the snow balls on his feet, get off his back and find you a sharp-edged rock or a sharp stick and knock the snowballs from his feet. If he falls with you and hurts you—what are we going to do then?"

Mom looked serious when she spoke to me. I wasn't afraid of Fred falling with me. I was glad to get on my way. I wasn't afraid. I wanted to ride Fred to town. It was the first time in my life that I had ever been allowed to ride to town to sell anything.

"You get a sack of meal if you sell a basket," Mom said. "It will cost you fifty cents. If you sell all your baskets, get a sack of flour too. That's a dollar. That will make a dollar and a half. You'll have a dollar and forty-five cents left. Get a quarter's worth of salt, a quarter's worth of sugar and a small bucket of lard. If you have a penny left, bring it home to me; I've got a use for every penny."

I tied the basket handles together and put two baskets on each side of me behind the saddle. I pulled my toboggan cap low over my ears and rode Fred up the hollow toward Greenup. My feet were warm in my wool socks and brogan shoes. The cold wind hit my face as I rode away in the winter morning mists. Mom stood in the door and watched me out of sight. I rode up the dark hollow where frost filled the air and where the rough sides of the black-oak trees that stood on the rocky bluffs were white with frost and looked like shadowy ghosts. The frozen snow crunched beneath Fred's big feet.

As I rode over the hill toward the town, a man was feeding his cattle.

"Would you like to buy a basket, Mister?" I asked.

"How do you sell them, Sonnie?" he asked.

"Thirty-five cents for the peck basket," I said. "Sixty cents for the half-bushel basket and a dollar apiece for the bushel baskets."

"I'll take both of the bushel baskets," he said as he pulled his billfold from his pocket and reached me two one-dollar bills. I untied the baskets from the saddle and gave them to him. Two dollars in my pocket and two baskets to sell. The next log shack I passed, I climbed down from my saddle and knocked at the door. A man came to the door.

"Do you want to buy a basket, Mister?" I asked.

"Sonnie, it's cold weather to sell baskets, isn't it?" he said. "You're out awfully early too. What time did you start this morning?"

"Daylight."

As we talked, the man stepped out into the yard and looked at my baskets. He asked me the price and I told him.

"I'll take both your baskets," he said. "These are well-made baskets and I need feed baskets. I'll take a couple of bushel baskets if you'll make them for me."

"I'll bring 'em to you in two days from now," I said, "if I live and Mom lives."

"Does your mother make these baskets?"

"Yes."

"She certainly put them together well," he said. "I've made baskets and I know a basket."

I said good-by to the tall beardy-faced man. I felt good to take Pa's place and go to town. I felt like I was helping run the place. I got off Fred's back twice and knocked the balls of snow from his feet with a stick. I rode to town and got my meal and flour. I put a sack of flour in one end of a coffee sack and a sack of meal in the other and balanced it across Fred's broad back—tied the coffee sack to a ring in my saddle. I carried the sugar, salt and lard in another sack in front of my saddle. Slowly, I went over the hill home.

When I rode back home, Mom came out the front door to meet me. I showed her my meal, flour, sugar, salt and lard. Mom's face brightened with a smile. She stood beside the horse and held the bridle reins when I climbed from the saddle a little stiff with cold.

"And here's twenty-five cents left," I said as I pulled my mitten from my right hand and pulled a quarter from my pocket.

"We'll make it," Mom said. "The winter is dark now but after a while spring will come. Violets are budding under the dead leaves beneath the snow right now!"

When I went to the woods to haul wood for the fireplace and the kitchen stove, Mom put on Pa's clothes and went with me. Pa's boots fit tightly on Mom's legs. Mom's long slender body fit well in Pa's corduroy pants. His coat was not too broad for Mom's shoulders.

I tied Fred to a tree by his bridle rein. Then Mom and I took the double-bitted ax and the crosscut saw down to a tall dead oak. I cut a notch part of the way into the dead tree the way I wanted it to fall. Mom took the ax and finished chopping the notch. We got down on our knees together and pulled the long crosscut saw through the hard dead oak tree. After we sawed awhile, we heard a crack and the tree bent earthward and hit the snow-covered hill below with a slash. The snow dashed in a white powdery cloud high into the air. I took the ax and trimmed the knots from the tree while Mom led Fred up to the tree, hooked the snaking chain around the log and fastened the trace chains to the singletree.

"He's ready," Mom said.

I climbed on Fred's back and reined him with the bridle reins down the path. Clouds of snow blew from under Fred's feet as he moved the big dead log toward the woodyard. Mom followed with the ax in her ungloved hand and the crosscut saw across her shoulder. When Fred got to the woodyard, he stopped. I got off his back—unhitched the traces and took him to the barn. I came back to the woodyard. All afternoon Mom got down on her knees in the snow on one side of the log and I got down on the other side of the big dead log. We dragged the crosscut saw across the bone-dry seasoned oak log. We cut stovewood lengths and firewood lengths until we finished the log. Then we split the wood lengths with our axes. I used my pole-ax on the stovewood lengths for the cookstove. Mom used the double-bitted ax and split the longer firewood lengths. After we split the lengths into finer wood, I carried it and stacked it in the entry where it was safe from rain, sleet and snow.

"When your Pa gets well again," Mom said, "I won't have so much work to do. He always took care of the wood getting."

Mom would sit up on the long winter evenings when the wind blew around the house and weave baskets. Sophie would often help her with the white-oak splits after she had washed the supper dishes. Sophie would take the case knife and smooth the splinters from the splits. I would take the drawing knife and rip off long splits from the white-oak sapling lengths. It was fun for us to do this around the winter fire while we laughed and talked and parched corn in a skillet. Mary parched the corn while Sophie and I helped Mom. Pa lay in bed—his face pale on the white pillow in the dim flicker of the pine torch above our mantel and the leaping blazes from the forestick.

Sometimes Pa talked to us about spring and when he would be plowing again. He told us he'd never plant the swamps in the hollow again and have the craw-dads to cut down the young corn soon as it sprouted from the furrow. One day when Mom worked steadily all day and Sophie and I helped her in the evening, she made twelve baskets.

"It's one of the biggest day's work I've ever done in my life," Mom said. "If I could make twelve baskets one day with another, your Pa wouldn't have to worry about spring and plowing."

"Mom wanted me to be careful about the horse falling," I thought. "She told me to keep the snow knocked from his feet so it wouldn't ball and throw him when I rode him to Greenwood—Mom doesn't know what she would do without me—well, she'd better watch about making twelve baskets one day with another. What would we do if Mom would get sick?"

As I walked toward the barn over the frozen snow, I had these thoughts about my mother.

Every weekday, I took baskets to Greenwood. I sold them almost any place I stopped. When I sold all my baskets one day, I learned to take orders for the next day. There was a ready sale for the baskets my mother made. And I learned to be a good salesman for a boy of ten. After I'd go to Greenup in the morning and sell baskets and bring back the things Mom told me to get, I'd climb the bluff above the hog pen and cut the bushy-topped white-oak saplings and slide them over the bluff to the barn. Then I'd carry them to the entry and saw them into lengths with a handsaw, split them into quarters and carry them into the house for Mom.

When our feed ran out, Mom sent me to Broughton's to see about feed.

"I think John Broughton's got corn and I know he's got fodder to sell," Mom said. "You get the saddle on Fred and ride out there and see. Don't pay over twenty cents a shock for fodder. Offer him fifteen cents at first and if he won't take that, then offer him twenty cents. We have to have feed for Fred and Gypsy. Offer him ninety cents a barrel for corn and don't give him over a dollar a barrel."

When I rode away to Broughton's to see about feed, I left Mom at home making baskets. I rode down the hollow and turned up the left fork of Ragweed Hollow. The snow was nearly to Fred's neck in places. I found my way to Broughton's barn where Mr. Broughton was feeding his cows.

"I'll take fifteen cents a shock for thirty shocks of fodder," Mr. Broughton said. "That's all I have to sell. That ought to winter your horse and cow until grass gets here this spring. I won't take ninety cents a barrel for my corn. I'll take a dollar a barrel for it and put it in your corncrib. I can let you have ten barrels of corn."

"All right, Mr. Broughton," I said. "I'll pay you for the corn and fodder right now if you'll promise me you'll deliver the fodder while you're bringing the corn."

Mr. Broughton's eyes looked big when I told him I'd pay him now. I know he wondered where I got the money. He knew Pa was sick, for he had been around home a couple of times to see him and talked to him far into the night. I paid Mr. Broughton a ten-dollar bill, four one-dollar bills, and I gave him a half-dollar, and then I rode toward home. The next day we had feed in our barn to last until the hills got green again.

"How's the feed holding out?" Pa asked.

"Mick, we've got plenty of feed."

"That feed's lasting the longest of any feed yet."

"We've got enough to last until the pastures get green."

Pa would curve his thin lips in a smile. He would lie on the bed and ask questions about the horse, cow and the chickens.

Often when I walked along the creek I found rabbits dead—frozen hard as an icicle. I found dead quails. I found dead possums. Maybe they had starved to death for something to eat. I found still life wherever I went. The weather had been so cold and all life had shrunk to the bone, perished for food or had frozen to death.

The snow didn't show any signs of melting. All we did at home was get wood, feed the horse and cow, cook, eat, sleep and make baskets. I took four, six, eight and often ten baskets away each day to Greenup. People called me the "Basket Boy." I brought back meal, flour, lard and groceries. Every day I brought back a piece of dry goods for Mom. She'd write down on paper what she wanted and I'd bring it back. Each day I brought back some money to Mom. I never spent all that I got for the baskets. Mom planned the spending so I'd bring the money home.

"A body needs a little money about the house," Mom said. "We never know what time we might need it. I've got to keep a little ahead to buy medicine for your Pa. He's liable to get worse any time. It's hard to tell. He's had a long lingering spell this winter and his face is awful white. His jawbones look like they'll come through the skin any minute, his face is so thin."

As the winter days dragged on toward spring and the great sheets of snow remained on the steep hill slopes, Mom did not go to the woodyard and help me cut wood like she had. I cut the wood with my pole-ax. Mom sat in her chair before the fire and wove baskets. She seldom got up for anything. Pa talked more to Mom now than he had ever talked. She propped him up in bed with his pillow behind his back and he watched her weave baskets. He talked to her about when the snow would leave and the ground would show—dark with melted snow-water running down over the hills leaping like fish in the sunlight.

"Go to Greenwood and get the Doctor," Mom said one day. "Get on Fred and hurry to town!"

"Is Pa worse?" I asked.

"Don't ask questions but hurry," Mom said.

I rode Fred over the snow fast as I could go. I got Doctor Morris out of bed. He rode his horse and we raced back over the snow in the winter moonlight and starlight. When we got to the house, I saw a light from the front window. Sophie met me at the front door and told me that we'd have to sit by a fire in the kitchen stove. Doctor Morris went into the house.

It was some time before daylight when I heard a baby cry.

"I hear a baby crying, Sophie," I said.

"Yes, didn't you know?"

"But I never would have thought that."

"Come in the front room, you children," Doctor Morris said as he looked in at the kitchen door. "You will be very happy when you see the big fine brother I have brought you."

Sophie and I ran into the room to see our brother. We had a lamp in our front room now. I could understand why Mom had me to buy it. I could understand about the cloth she had me to get. I thought of these things as I looked at Mom lying on the bed with the quilts turned down enough for us to see our brother. We stood beside the bed watching the quilts shake when he kicked. And he cried like he was mad at everybody. There was a smile on Mom's lips.

It was March and the sun had shone brightly for three days. The snow melted and the snow-water ran in tiny streams down the small drains on the steep bluffs.

When Pop saw the dark hills again he sat up in bed. There was more color in his face now. Each day he looked at the hills and talked to Mom. Soon as Mom got up from the bed, Pa was up walking about. Color was coming back rapidly to his face. Flesh was coming back to his skeleton body. Sophie did the cooking and I did the feeding. I got the wood. Mom had paid all of our bills and she had a little money left after she paid Doctor Morris.

"All our debts are paid, Mick," Mom said. "The hard winter is over. Violets are in bloom and pasture grass is coming back to the pastures."

Mom stood in the late March wind with our tiny brother wrapped in a blanket in her arms. She kicked the dead leaves away with the toe of her shoe from a clump of blooming violets. I walked ahead of Pa and cut stalks and sprouts with a grubbing hoe. Pa rested between the handles of the plow and looked at Mom standing at the edge of the field with the early buds of spring about her.

About the author

Jesse Stuart (1907–   ) was born and brought up in the hills of Kentucky. In *The Thread That Runs So True* he tells of his boyhood and his early days of teaching in the schools of Kentucky and Ohio. Mr. Stuart no longer teaches but spends much of his time in writing stories, poetry, and biography.

Questions for discussion

1. The boy tells the story. Is he the main character, or is his mother? Support your answer by referring to the story.
2. The author makes clear that this was a very severe winter. Point out the details he uses to make this clear.
3. Does it seem reasonable that Mom could make such a fine quality of baskets? What clues at the beginning point up her skill and experience?
4. Were you surprised to learn about the birth of the baby? Look back and find the clues that point to this event.
5. What is the significance in the story of Mom's saying to Pa, "The sun will shine on blue violets under the last year's leaves."? Where else do the blue violets come into the story?

6. POINT OF VIEW. The story is told in the first person, but it is told objectively. That is, you are told what the characters said and did, but you are not told how they *felt* about their situation. Nevertheless, you know how they must have felt.
   a. What do you think Mom's feeling was at the beginning of the story? What do you think her feelings were when the boy came back from selling the first baskets? What were her feelings at the end of the story?
   b. What do you think Pa's feelings were at the start of the story? At the close of the story (see last paragraph)? Why do you think "Pa talked more to Mom now than he ever talked"?
   c. Can you find two places in which the boy says something about his feelings? Do you know how he felt about the heavy winter work?
7. The conflict in the story is between the family and the hard winter. In what other stories in this book do you find a similar conflict? At what point does it seem clear that the family will win out?

Vocabulary growth

VARIANT MEANINGS. The word *dog-trot* is used here to refer to the space between two buildings. To people of the Kentucky hills, a *dog-trot* is any space where dogs can exercise and still not be at large. What other meaning does dog-trot have?

"She put her small white hand upon a big oak backlog." What is a *backlog*? You may have to consult the dictionary and find out. What is a *backlog* of orders in business? What is the connection between the two kinds of backlogs? Which meaning do you think arose first?

For composition

1. What thoughts were going through the minds of the characters in this story? Take one of the following situations and write a paragraph that tells how the characters *felt* about the situation:
   a. "If your father was only well," Mom said—"You children run along and play. Leave me alone to think."
   b. "I passed the water hole and the empty hog-pen."
   c. "Pa rested between the handles of the plow and looked at Mom standing at the edge of the field with the early buds of spring about her."

The Sniper

LIAM O'FLAHERTY

In the 1920's, civil war broke out in Ireland. The question was whether the country should be a Free State within the British Commonwealth, or a completely independent nation. Families were divided, and friend was set against friend. Property was destroyed and blood was shed.

The story below is set in these dark and troubled times. To the solitary sniper on the roof top it was all an exciting game until—

THE long June twilight faded into night. Dublin lay enveloped in darkness, but for the dim light of the moon, that shone through fleecy clouds, casting a pale light as of approaching dawn over the streets and the dark waters of the Liffey. Around the beleaguered Four Courts the heavy guns roared. Here and there through the city machine guns and rifles broke the silence of the night, spasmodically, like dogs barking on lone farms. Republicans and Free Staters were waging civil war.

On a rooftop near O'Connell Bridge, a Republican sniper lay watching. Beside him lay his rifle and over his shoulders were slung a pair of field-glasses. His face was the face of a student—thin and ascetic, but his eyes had the cold gleam of the fanatic. They were deep and thoughtful, the eyes of a man, who is used to look at death.

He was eating a sandwich hungrily. He had eaten nothing since morning. He had been too excited to eat. He finished the sandwich, and taking a flask of whiskey from his pocket, he took a short draught. Then he returned the flask to his pocket. He paused for a moment, considering whether he should risk a smoke. It was dangerous. The flash might be seen in the darkness and there were enemies watching. He decided to take the risk. Placing a cigarette between his lips, he struck a match, inhaled the smoke hurriedly and put out the light. Almost immediately, a bullet flattened itself against the parapet

199

of the roof. The sniper took another whiff and put out the cigarette. Then he swore softly and crawled away to the left.

Cautiously he raised himself and peered over the parapet. There was a flash and a bullet whizzed over his head. He dropped immediately. He had seen the flash. It came from the opposite side of the street.

He rolled over the roof to a chimney stack in the rear, and slowly drew himself up behind it, until his eyes were level with the top of the parapet. There was nothing to be seen—just the dim outline of the opposite housetop against the blue sky. His enemy was under cover.

Just then an armoured car came across the bridge and advanced slowly up the street. It stopped on the opposite side of the street fifty yards ahead. The sniper could hear the dull panting of the motor. His heart beat faster. It was an enemy car. He wanted to fire, but he knew it was useless. His bullets would never pierce the steel that covered the grey monster.

Then round the corner of a side street came an old woman, her head covered by a tattered shawl. She began to talk to the man in the turret of the car. She was pointing to the roof where the sniper lay. An informer.

The turret opened. A man's head and shoulders appeared, looking towards the sniper. The sniper raised his rifle and fired. The head fell heavily on the turret wall. The woman darted toward the side street. The sniper fired again. The woman whirled round and fell with a shriek into the gutter.

Suddenly from the opposite roof a shot rang out and the sniper dropped his rifle with a curse. The rifle clattered to the roof. The sniper thought the noise would wake the dead. He stooped to pick the rifle up. He couldn't lift it. His forearm was dead. "I'm hit," he muttered.

Dropping flat on to the roof, he crawled back to the parapet. With his left hand he felt the injured right forearm. The blood was oozing through the sleeve of his coat. There was no pain—just a deadened sensation, as if the arm had been cut off.

Quickly he drew his knife from his pocket, opened it on the breastwork of the parapet and ripped open the sleeve. There was a small hole where the bullet had entered. On the other side there was no hole. The bullet had lodged in the bone. It must have fractured it. He bent the arm below the wound. The arm bent back easily. He ground his teeth to overcome the pain.

Then, taking out his field dressing, he ripped open the packet with his knife. He broke the neck of the iodine bottle and let the bitter fluid drip into the wound. A paroxysm of pain swept through him. He placed the cotton wadding over the wound and wrapped the dressing over it. He tied the end with his teeth.

Then he lay still against the parapet, and closing his eyes, he made an effort of will to overcome the pain.

In the street beneath all was still. The armoured car had retired speedily over the bridge, with the machine gunner's head hanging lifeless over the turret. The woman's corpse lay still in the gutter.

The sniper lay for a long time nursing his wounded arm and planning escape. Morning must not find him wounded on the roof. The enemy on the opposite roof covered his escape. He must kill that enemy and he could not use his rifle. He had only a revolver to do it. Then he thought of a plan.

Taking off his cap, he placed it over the muzzle of his rifle. Then he pushed the rifle slowly upwards over the parapet, until the cap was visible from the opposite side of the street. Almost immediately there was a report, and a bullet pierced the center of the cap. The sniper slanted the rifle forward. The cap slipped down into the street. Then, catching the rifle in the middle, the sniper dropped his left hand over the roof and let it hang, lifelessly. After a few moments he let the rifle drop to the street. Then he sank to the roof, dragging his hand with him.

Crawling quickly to the left, he peered up at the corner of the roof. His ruse had succeeded. The other sniper, seeing the cap and rifle fall, thought that he had killed his man. He was now standing before a row of chimney pots, looking across, with his head clearly silhouetted against the western sky.

The Republican sniper smiled and lifted his revolver above the edge of the parapet. The distance was about fifty yards—a hard shot in the dim light, and his right arm was paining him like a thousand devils. He took a steady aim. His hand trembled with eagerness. Pressing his lips together, he took a deep breath through his nostrils and fired. He was almost deafened with the report and his arm shook with the recoil.

Then, when the smoke cleared, he peered across and uttered a cry of joy. His enemy had been hit. He was reeling over the parapet in his death agony. He struggled to keep his feet, but he was slowly falling forward, as if in a dream. The rifle fell from his grasp, hit the parapet, fell over, bounded off the pole of a barber's shop beneath and then cluttered on to the pavement.

Then the dying man on the roof crumpled up and fell forward. The body turned over and over in space and hit the ground with a dull thud. Then it lay still.

The sniper looked at his enemy falling and he shuddered. The lust of battle died in him. He became bitten by remorse. The sweat stood out in beads on his forehead. Weakened by his wound and the long summer day of fasting and watching on the roof, he revolted from the sight of the shattered mass of his dead enemy. His teeth chattered. He began to gibber to himself, cursing the war, cursing himself, cursing everybody.

He looked at the smoking revolver in his hand and with an oath he hurled it to the roof at his feet. The revolver went off with the concussion, and the bullet whizzed past the sniper's head. He was frightened back to his senses by the shock. His nerves steadied. The cloud of fear scattered from his mind and he laughed.

Taking the whiskey flask from his pocket, he emptied it at a draught. He felt reckless under the influence of the spirits. He decided to leave the roof and look for his company commander to report. Everywhere around was quiet. There was not much danger in going through the streets. He picked up his revolver and put it in his pocket. Then he crawled down through the skylight to the house underneath.

When the sniper reached the laneway on the street level, he felt a sudden curiosity as to the identity of the enemy sniper whom he had killed. He decided that he was a good shot whoever he was. He wondered if he knew him. Perhaps he had been in his own company before the split in the army. He decided to risk going over to have a look at him. He peered around the corner into O'Connell Street. In the upper part of the street there was heavy firing, but around here all was quiet.

The sniper darted across the street. A machine gun tore up the ground around him with a hail of bullets, but he escaped. He threw himself face downwards beside the corpse. The machine gun stopped.

Then the sniper turned over the dead body and looked into his brother's face.

About the author

Liam O'Flaherty (1896–   ) was born on the Aran Islands of Ireland. He originally planned to study for the priesthood, but having a change of heart, he entered University College, Dublin. At this time, World War I was in progress, and O'Flaherty decided to leave school and join the Irish Guards. He spent six months on the Western Front, seeing for himself the tragedy of war. At its conclusion, O'Flaherty embarked on a trip around the world, making his way as a stoker, a deckhand, a beachcomber and a lumberjack. O'Flaherty writes with a special compassion for the common man, but he is also able to write keen psychological studies of troubled individuals. His great novel, *The Informer*, a highly charged adventure story of Ireland's struggle for independence, has become a film classic.

Questions for discussion

1. There is a sharp contrast between the killing of the sniper's first two victims and the killing of the "enemy" on the roof top across the way. Did you see it? What is the difference between the duel with this "enemy" and the killing of the old woman in the street? What is there about a sniper's job that seems revolting?
2. What sort of man was the sniper at the start of the story? Reread the paragraphs down to, "Then he thought of a plan." What do these items disclose:
    a. The look in his eyes.
    b. Killing an old woman in cold blood.
    c. The dressing of his wounded arm.
3. What was the effect upon the sniper of his success in killing the enemy across the roof tops? He suddenly began hating something. What was it?
4. After his success, the sniper's character seemed to change. Does this change last? How can you tell?
5. The sniper did not give a second thought to the old woman, or to the man in the car whom he had killed. Why was he so curious about the other sniper he had killed? Why did he go out into the street to look at him? Does this suggest a reason for his earlier remorse for having killed the man?
6. What did you think of the ending? Reread the notes that precede the story. Does the end of the story seem reasonable? How else might it have ended? Why is the ending of the story so dramatic? In answering this question, keep in mind the sniper's attitude as he left the rooftop.
7. What is the theme or underlying idea of the story?

Vocabulary growth

WORDS ARE INTERESTING. It is interesting to speculate about the history of some words. A word such as *ascetic,* for instance, has an interesting background. It means "self-denying" or "austere," and it comes from a Greek word meaning "to exercise, or to train as an athlete does." Today people think of an *ascetic* as one who denies himself pleasures and comforts for religious reasons. Athletes in training have to deny themselves certain things in order to stay in condition. Ascetics and athletes thus have something in common.

A *beleaguered* city is one that is surrounded by enemy forces. The *league* part of the word comes from a Latin word meaning "camp." In short, when a military force camps around a city to prevent anyone from entering or leaving, that city is *beleaguered.*

WORD PARTS. The prefix *para-* has many different meanings, one of which is "to guard" or "protect." It has this meaning in *parapet.* The *pet* part of the word comes from an Italian word *petto,* meaning "breast." In military affairs a parapet is a structure that protects the soldier's breast from enemy fire. What other meaning does parapet have? Consult your dictionary. Find two other common words in which *para-* also means "protect."

For composition

1. What happened to the sniper? Did he go back to report to his company commander? Did he leave the army? Write two paragraphs in the same style as the story to describe what finally happens to the sniper.

2. Assume that the sniper has quit the war. He is writing a letter of explanation to his former company commander. He begins, "I make no apology. I have had enough of war. No man has given more to the cause . . ." Write the rest of the report.

Two Soldiers

WILLIAM FAULKNER

The author of this story was awarded the Nobel prize for literature in 1950. In his acceptance speech he said that the writer of today must write of "the old verities and truths of the heart—love and honor and pity and pride and compassion and sacrifice." You may expect to find some of these truths as you now turn back to December, 1941, and get acquainted with the Grier family—especially with Pete Grier's younger brother who tells the story.

ME and Pete would go down to Old Man Killegrew's and listen to his radio. We would wait until after supper, after dark, and we would stand outside Old Man Killegrew's parlor window, and we could hear it because Old Man Killegrew's wife was deaf, and so he run the radio as loud as it would run, and so me and Pete could hear it plain as Old Man Killegrew's wife could, I reckon, even standing outside with the window closed.

And that night I said, "What? Japanese? What's a pearl harbor?" and Pete said, "Hush."

And so we stood there; it was cold, listening to the fellow in the radio talking, only I couldn't make no heads nor tails out of it. Then the fellow said that would be all for a while, and me and Pete walked back up the road to home, and Pete told me what it was. Because he was nigh twenty and he had done finished the Consolidated last June and he knowed a heap: about them Japanese dropping bombs on Pearl Harbor and that Pearl Harbor was across the water.

"Across what water?" I said. "Across that Government reservoy up at Oxford?"

"Naw," Pete said. "Across the big water. The Pacific Ocean."

We went home. Maw and pap was already asleep and me and Pete laid in bed, and I still couldn't understand where it was, and Pete told me again—the Pacific Ocean.

"What's the matter with you?" Pete said. "You're going on nine years old. You been in school now ever since September. Ain't you learned nothing yet?"

"I reckon we ain't got as fer as the Pacific Ocean yet," I said.

We was still sowing the vetch then that ought to been all finished by the fifteenth of November, because pap was still behind, just like he had been ever since me and Pete had knowed him. And we had firewood to git in, too, but every night me and Pete would go down to Old Man Killegrew's and stand outside his parlor window in the cold and listen to his radio; then we would come back home and lay in bed and Pete would tell me what it was. That is, he would tell me for a while. Then he wouldn't tell me. It was like he didn't want to talk about it no more. He would tell me to shut up because he wanted to go to sleep, but he never wanted to go to sleep.

He would lay there, a heap stiller than if he was asleep, and it would be something, I could feel it coming out of him, like he was mad at me, or like he was worried about something, and it wasn't that neither, because he never had nothing to worry about. He never got behind like pap, let alone stayed behind. Pap give him ten acres when he graduated from the Consolidated, and me and Pete both reckoned pap was durn glad to get shut of at least ten acres, less to have to worry about himself; and Pete had them ten acres all sowed to vetch and busted out and bedded for the winter, and so it wasn't that. But it was something. And still we would go down to Old Man Killegrew's every night and listen to his radio, and they was at it in the Philippines now, but General MacArthur was holding um. Then we would come back home and lay in the bed, and Pete wouldn't tell me nothing or talk at all. He would just lay there still as an ambush and when I would touch him, his side or his leg would feel hard and still as iron, until after a while and I would go to sleep.

Then one night—it was the first time he had said nothing to me except to jump on me about not chopping enough wood at the wood tree where he was cutting—he said, "I got to go."

"Go where?" I said.

"To that war," Pete said.

"Before we even finish gettin' in the firewood?"

"Firewood, heck," Pete said.

"All right," I said. "When we going to start?"

But he wasn't even listening. He laid there, hard and still as iron in the dark. "I got to go," he said. "I jest ain't going to put up with no folks treating the Unity States that way."

"Yes," I said. "Firewood or no firewood, I reckon we got to go."

This time he heard me. He laid still again, but it was a different kind of still.

"You?" he said. "To a war?"

"You'll whup the big uns and I'll whup the little uns," I said.

Then he told me I couldn't go. At first I thought he just never wanted me tagging after him, like he wouldn't leave me go with him when he went sparking them girls of Tull's. Then he told me the Army wouldn't leave me go because I was too little, and then I knowed he really meant it and that I couldn't go nohow noways. And somehow I hadn't believed until then that he was going himself, but now I knowed he was and that he wasn't going to leave me go with him a-tall.

"I'll chop the wood and tote the water for you-all then!" I said. "You got to have wood and water!"

Anyway, he was listening to me now. He wasn't like iron now.

He turned onto his side and put his hand on my chest because it was me that was laying straight and hard on my back now.

"No," he said. "You got to stay here and help pap."

"Help him what?" I said. "He ain't never caught up nohow. He can't get no further behind. He can sholy take care of this little shirttail of a farm while me and you are whupping them Japanese. I got to go too. If you got to go, then so have I."

"No," Pete said. "Hush now. Hush." And he meant it, and I knowed he did. Only I made sho from his own mouth. I quit.

"So I just can't go then," I said.

"No," Pete said. "You just can't go. You're too little, in the first place, and in the second place—"

"All right," I said. "Then shut up and leave me to go to sleep."

So he hushed then and laid back. And I laid there like I was already asleep, and pretty soon he was asleep and I knowed it was the wanting to go to the war that had worried him and kept him awake, and now that he had decided to go, he wasn't worried any more.

The next morning he told maw and pap. Maw was all right. She cried.

"No," she said, crying, "I don't want him to go. I would rather go myself in his place, if I could. I don't want to save the country.

Them Japanese could take it all and keep it, so long as they left me and my family and my children alone. But I remember my brother Marsh in that other war. He had to go to that one when he wasn't but nineteen and our mother couldn't understand it then any more than I can now. But she told Marsh if he had to go, he had to go. And so, if Pete's got to go to this one, he's got to go to it. Jest don't ask me to understand why."

But pap was the one. He was the feller. "To the war?" he said. "Why I don't see a bit of use in that. You ain't old enough for the draft, and the country ain't being invaded. Our President in Washington, D.C., is watching the conditions and he will notify us. Besides, in that other war your ma just mentioned, I was drafted and sent clean to Texas and was held there nigh eight months until they finally quit fighting. It seems to me that that, along with your Uncle Marsh who received a actual wound on the battlefields of France, is enough for me and mine to have to do to protect the country, at least in my lifetime. Besides, what'll I do for help on the farm with you gone? It seems to me I'll get mighty far behind."

"You been behind as long as I can remember," Pete said. "Anyway I'm going. I got to."

"Of course he's got to go," I said. "Them Japanese—"

"You hush your mouth!" maw said, crying. "Nobody's talking to you! Go and get ma a armful of wood! That's what you can do!"

So I got the wood. And all the next day, while me and Pete and pap was getting in as much wood as we could in that time because Pete said how pap's idea of plenty of wood was one more stick laying against the wall that maw ain't put on the fire yet, maw was getting Pete ready to go. She washed and mended his clothes and cooked him a shoe box of vittles. And that night me and Pete laid in the bed and listened to her packing his grip and crying, until after a while Pete got up in his nightshirt and went back there, and I could hear them talking, until at last maw said, "You ought to go, and so I want you to go. But I don't understand it, and I won't never, and so don't expect me to." And Pete come back and got into bed again and laid again still and hard as iron on his back, and then he said, and he wasn't talking to me, he wasn't talking to nobody: "I got to go. I just got to."

"Sho you got to," I said. "Them Japanese—" He turned over hard, he kind of surged over onto his side, looking at me in the dark.

"Anyway, you're all right," he said. "I expected to have more trouble with you than with all the rest of them put together."

"I reckon I can't help it neither," I said. "But maybe it will run a few years longer and I can get there. Maybe someday I will jest walk in on you."

"I hope not," Pete said. "Folks don't go to wars for fun. A man don't leave his maw crying just for fun."

"Then why are you going?" I said.

"I got to," he said. "I just got to. Now you go on to sleep. I got to ketch that early bus in the morning."

"All right," I said, "I hear tell Memphis is a big place. How will you find where the Army's at?"

"I'll ask somebody where to go to join it," Pete said. "Go on to sleep now."

"Is that what you'll ask for? Where to join the Army?" I said.

"Yes," Pete said. He turned onto his back again. "Shut up and go to sleep."

We went to sleep. The next morning we et breakfast by lamplight because the bus would pass at six o'clock. Maw wasn't crying now. She jest looked grim and busy, putting breakfast on the table while we et it. Then she finished packing Pete's grip, except he never wanted to take no grip to the war, but maw said decent folks never went nowhere, not even to a war, without a change of clothes and something to tote them in. She put in the shoe box of fried chicken and biscuits and she put the Bible in, too, and then it was time to go. We didn't know until then that maw wasn't going to the bus. She jest brought Pete's cap and overcoat, and still she didn't cry no more, she jest stood with her hands on Pete's shoulders and she didn't move, but somehow, and just holding Pete's shoulders, she looked as hard and fierce as when Pete had turned toward me in the bed last night and tole me that anyway I was all right.

"They could take the country and keep the country, as long as they never bothered me and mine," she said. Then she said, "Don't never forget who you are. You ain't rich and the rest of the world outside of Frenchman's Bend never heard of you. But your blood is good as any blood anywhere, and don't you never forget it."

Then she kissed him, and then we was out of the house, with pap toting Pete's grip whether Pete wanted him to or not. There wasn't no dawn even yet not even after we had stood on the highway by the mailbox, awhile. Then we seen the lights of the bus coming and I was watching the bus until it come up and Pete flagged it, and then, sho enough, there was daylight—it had started while I wasn't watching. And now me and Pete expected pap to say something else foolish, like he done before about how Uncle Marsh getting wounded in France and that trip to Texas pap had taken in 1918 ought to be enough to save the Unity States in 1942 but he never. He done all right too. He jest said, "Good-by, son. Always remember what your ma told you and write her whenever you find the time." Then he shaken Pete's hand, and Pete looked at me for a minute and put his hand on my head and rubbed my head durn nigh hard enough to wring my neck off and jumped into the bus, and the feller wound the door shut and the bus began to hum; then it was moving, humming and grinding and whining louder and louder; it was going fast, with two little red lights behind it that never seemed to get no littler, but jest seemed to be running together until pretty soon they would touch and jest be one light. But they never did, and then the bus was gone, and even like it was, I could have pretty nigh busted out crying, nigh to nine years old and all.

Me and pap went back to the house. All that day we worked at the wood tree, and so I never had no good chance until about middle of the afternoon. Then I taken my slingshot and I would have liked to took all my bird eggs, too, because Pete had give me his collection and he holp me with mine, and he would like to git the box out and look at them as good as I would, even if he was nigh twenty years old. But the box was too big to tote a long ways and have to worry with, so I just taken the shikepoke egg, because it was the best un, and wropped it up good into a matchbox and hid it and the slingshot under the corner of the barn. Then we et supper and went to bed, and I thought then how if I would 'a' had to stayed in that room and that bed like that even for one more night, I jest couldn't 'a' stood it. Then I could hear pap snoring, but I never heard no sound from maw, whether she was asleep or not, and I don't reckon she was. So I taken my shoes and drapped them out the window, and then I clumb out like I used to watch Pete do when he was still jest seventeen and pap wouldn't leave him out, and I put on my shoes and went to the barn and got the slingshot and the shikepoke egg and went to the highway.

It wasn't cold, it was just durn confounded dark, and that highway stretched on in front of me like, without nobody using it, it had stretched out half again as fer just like a man does when he lays down, so that for a time it looked like full sun was going to ketch me before I had finished them twenty-two miles to Jefferson. But it didn't. Daybreak was jest starting when I walked up the hill into town. I could smell breakfast cooking in the cabins and I wished I had thought to brought me a cold biscuit, but that was too late now. And Pete had told me Memphis was a piece beyond Jefferson, but I never knowed it was no eighty miles. So I stood there on that empty square, with daylight coming and coming and the street lights still burning and that Law looking down at me, and me still eighty miles from Memphis, and it had took me all night to walk jest twenty-two miles, and so, by the time I got to Memphis at that rate, Pete would 'a' done already started for Pearl Harbor.

"Where do you come from?" the Law said. And I told him again. "I got to git to Memphis. My brother's there."

"You mean you ain't got any folks around here?" the Law said. "Nobody but that brother? What are you doing way off down here and your brother in Memphis?"

And I told him again, "I got to git to Memphis. I ain't got no time to waste talking about it and I ain't got time to walk it. I got to git there today."

"Come on here," the Law said.

We went down another street. And there was the bus, jest like when Pete got into it yestiddy morning, except there wasn't no lights on it now and it was empty. There was a regular bus dee-po like a railroad dee-po, with a ticket counter and a feller behind it, and the Law said, "Set down over there," and I set down on the bench, and the Law said, "I want to use your telephone," and he talked into the telephone a minute and put it down and said to the feller behind the ticket counter, "Keep your eye on him. I'll be back as soon as Mrs. Habersham can arrange to get herself up and dressed." He went out. I got up and went to the ticket counter.

"I want to go to Memphis," I said.

"You bet," the feller said. "You set down on the bench now. Mr. Foote will be back in a minute."

"I don't know no Mr. Foote," I said. "I want to ride that bus to Memphis."

"You got some money?" he said. "It'll cost seventy-two cents."

I taken out the matchbox and unwropped the shikepoke egg. "I'll swap you this for a ticket to Memphis," I said.

"What's that?" he said.

"It's a shikepoke egg," I said. "You never seen one before. It's worth a dollar. I'll take seventy-two cents fer it."

"No," he said, "the fellers that own that bus insist on a cash basis. If I started swapping tickets for bird eggs and livestock and such, they would fire me. You go and set down on the bench now, like Mr. Foote—"

I started for the door, but he caught me, he put one hand on the ticket counter and jumped over it and caught up with me and reached his hand out to ketch my shirt. I whupped out my pocket-knife and snapped it open.

"You put a hand on me and I'll cut it off," I said.

I tried to dodge him and run at the door, but he could move quicker than any grown man I ever see, quick as Pete almost. He cut me off and stood with his back against the door and one foot raised a little, and there wasn't no other way to get out. "Get back on that bench and stay there," he said.

And there wasn't no other way out. And he stood against the door. So I went back to the bench. And then it seemed like to me that dee-po was full of folks. There was that Law again, and there was two ladies in fur coats and their faces already painted. But they still looked like they had got up in a hurry and they still never liked it, a old one and a young one, looking down at me.

"He hasn't got an overcoat!" the old one said. "How in the world did he ever get down here by himself?"

"I ask you," the Law said. "I couldn't get nothing out of him except his brother is in Memphis and he wants to get back up there."

"That's right," I said. "I got to git to Memphis today."

"Of course you must," the old one said. "Are you sure you can find your brother when you get to Memphis?"

"I reckon I can," I said. "I ain't got but one and I have knowed him all my life. I reckon I will know him again when I see him."

The old one looked at me. "Somehow he doesn't look like he lives in Memphis," she said.

"He probably don't," the Law said. "You can't tell though. He might live anywhere, overhalls or not. This day and time they get scattered overnight from hope to breakfast; boys and girls, too, almost before they can walk good. He might have been in Missouri or Texas either yestiddy, for all we know. But he don't seem to have any doubt his brother is in Memphis. All I know to do is send him up there and leave him look."

"Yes," the old one said.

The young one set down on the bench by me and opened a hand satchel and taken out a artermatic writing pen and some papers.

"Now, honey," the old one said, "we're going to see that you find your brother, but we must have a case history for our files first. We want to know your name and your brother's name and where you were born and when your parents died."

"I don't need no case history neither," I said. "All I want is to git to Memphis. I got to git there today."

"You see?" the Law said. He said it almost like he enjoyed it. "That's what I told you."

"You're lucky, at that, Mrs. Habersham," the bus feller said. "I don't think he's got a gun on him, but he can open that knife fast enough to suit any man."

But the old one just stood there looking at me.

"Well," she said. "Well. I really don't know what to do."

"I do," the bus feller said. "I'm going to give him a ticket out of my own pocket, as a measure of protecting the company against riot and bloodshed. And when Mr. Foote tells the city board about it, it will be a civic matter and they will give me a medal too. Hey, Mr. Foote?"

But nobody paid him no mind. The old one still stood looking down at me. She said, "Well," again. Then she taken a dollar from her purse and give it to the bus feller. "I suppose he will travel on a child's ticket, won't he?"

"Wellum," the bus feller said, "I just don't know what the regulations would be. Likely I will be fired for not crating him and marking the crate Poison. But I'll risk it."

Then they were gone. Then the Law come back with a sandwich and give it to me.

"You're sure you can find that brother?" he said.

"I ain't yet convinced why not," I said. "If I don't see Pete first, he'll see me. He knows me, too."

Then the Law went out for good, too, and I et the sandwich. Then more folks come in and bought tickets, and then the bus feller said it was time to go, and I got into the bus just like Pete done, and we were gone.

I seen all the towns. I seen all of them. When the bus got to going good, I found out I was jest about wore out for sleep. But there was too much I hadn't never saw before. We run out of Jefferson and run past fields and woods, then we would run into another town and out of that un and past fields and woods again, and then into another town with stores and gins and water tanks, and we run along by the railroad for a spell and I seen the signal arm move, and then some more towns, and I was jest about plumb wore out for sleep, but I couldn't resk it. Then Memphis begun. It seemed like, to me, it went on for miles. We would pass a patch of stores and I would think that was sholy it and the bus would even stop. But it wouldn't be Memphis yet and we would go on again past water tanks and smokestacks on top of the mills, and if they was gins and sawmills, I never knowed there was that many and I never seen any that big, and where they got enough cotton and logs to run um I don't know.

Then I seen Memphis. I knowed I was right this time. It was standing up into the air. It looked like about a dozen whole towns bigger than Jefferson was set up on one edge in a field, standing up into the air higher than ara hill in all Yoknapatawpha County. Then we was in it, with the bus stopping every few feet, it seemed like to me, and cars rushing past on both sides of it and the streets crowded with folks from ever'where in town that day, until I didn't see how there could 'a' been nobody left in Mis'sippi a-tall to even sell me a bus ticket, let alone write out no case histories. Then the bus stopped. It was another bus dee-po, a heap bigger than the one in Jefferson. And I said, "All right. Where do folks join the Army?"

"What?" the bus feller said.

And I said it again, "Where do folks join the Army?"

"Oh," he said. Then he told me how to get there. I was afraid at first I wouldn't ketch on how to do in a town as big as Memphis. But I caught on all right. I never had to ask but twice more. Then I was there, and I was durn glad to git out of all them rushing cars and shoving folks and all that racket fer a spell, and I thought, it won't be long now, and I thought how if there was any kind of a crowd there that had done already joined the Army, too, Pete would likely see me before I seen him. And so I walked into the room. And Pete wasn't there.

He wasn't even there. There was a soldier with a big arrerhead on his sleeve, writing, and two fellers standing in front of him, and there was some more folks there, I reckon. It seems to me I remember some more folks there.

I went to the table where the soldier was writing, and I said, "Where's Pete?" and he looked up and I said, "My brother, Pete Grier. Where is he?"

"What?" the soldier said. "Who?"

And I told him again. "He joined the Army yestiddy. He's going to Pearl Harbor. So am I. I want to ketch him. Where you-all got him?" Now they were all looking at me, but I never paid them no mind. "Come on," I said. "Where is he?"

The soldier had quit writing. He had both hands spraddled out on the table. "Oh," he said. "You're going, too, hah?"

"Yes," I said. "They got to have wood and water. I can chop it and tote it. Come on. Where's Pete?"

The soldier stood up. "Who let you in here?" he said. "Go on. Beat it."

"Durn that," I said. "You tell me where Pete—"

I be dog if he couldn't move faster than the bus feller even. He never come over the table, he come around it, he was on me almost before I knowed it, so that I jest had time to jump back and whup out my pocketknife and snap it open and hit one lick, and he hollered and jumped back and grabbed one hand with the other and stood there cussing and hollering.

One of the other fellers grabbed me from behind, and I hit at him with the knife, but I couldn't reach him.

Then both of the fellers had me from behind, and then another soldier come out of a door at the back. He had on a belt with a britching strop over one shoulder.

"What's this?" he said.

"That little son cut me with a knife!" the first soldier hollered. When he said that I tried to git at him again, but both them fellers was holding me, two against one, and the soldier with the backing strop said, "Here, here. Put your knife up, feller. None of us are armed. A man don't knife-fight folks that are barehanded." I could begin to hear him then. He sounded jest like Pete talked to me. "Let him go," he said. They let me go. "Now what's all the trouble about?" And I told him. "I see," he said. "And you come up to see if he was all right before he left."

"No," I said. "I come to—"

But he had already turned to where the first soldier was wropping a handkerchief around his hand.

"Have you got him?" he said. The first soldier went back to the table and looked at some papers.

"Here he is," he said. "He enlisted yestiddy. He's in a detachment leaving this morning for Little Rock." He had a watch stropped on his arm. He looked at it. "The train leaves in about fifty minutes. If I know country boys, they're probably all down there at the station right now."

"Get him up here," the one with the backing strop said. "Phone the station. Tell the porter to get him a cab. And you come with me," he said.

It was another office behind that un, with jest a table and some chairs. We set there while the soldier smoked, and it wasn't long; I knowed Pete's feet soon as I heard them. Then the first soldier opened the door and Pete come in. He never had no soldier clothes on. He looked jest like he did when he got on the bus yestiddy morning, except it seemed to me like it was at least a week, so much had happened, and I had done had to do so much traveling. He come in and there he was, looking at me like he hadn't never left home, except that here we was in Memphis, on the way to Pearl Harbor.

"What in durnation are you doing here?" he said.

And I told him, "You got to have wood and water to cook with. I can chop it and tote it for you-all."

"No," Pete said. "You're going back home."

"No, Pete," I said. "I got to go too. I got to. It hurts my heart, Pete."

"No," Pete said. He looked at the soldier. "I jest don't know what could have happened to him, lootenant," he said. "He never drawed a knife on anybody before in his life."

He looked at me. "What did you do it for?"

"I don't know," I said. "I jest had to. I jest had to git here. I jest had to find you."

"Well, don't you never do it again, you hear?" Pete said. "You put that knife in your pocket and you keep it there. If I ever again hear of you drawing it on anybody, I'm coming back from wherever I am at and whup the fire out of you. You hear me?"

"I would pure cut a throat if it would bring you back to stay," I said. "Pete," I said. "Pete."

"No," Pete said. Now his voice wasn't hard and quick no more, it was almost quiet, and I knowed now I wouldn't never change him. "You must go home. You must look after maw, and I am depending on you to look after my ten acres. I want you to go back home. Today. Do you hear?"

"I hear," I said.

"Can he get back home by himself?" the soldier said.

"He come up here by himself," Pete said.

"I can get back, I reckon," I said. "I don't live in but one place. I don't reckon it's moved."

Pete taken a dollar out of his pocket and give it to me. "That'll buy your bus ticket right to our mailbox," he said. "I want you to mind the lootenant. He'll send you to the bus. And you go back home and you take care of maw and look after my ten acres and keep that durn knife in your pocket. You hear me?"

"Yes, Pete," I said.

"All right," Pete said. "Now I got to go." He put his hand on my head again. But this time he never wrung my neck. He just laid his hand on my head a minute. And then I be dog if he didn't lean down and kiss me, and I heard his feet and then the door, and I never looked up and that was all, me setting there, rubbing the place where Pete kissed me and the soldier throwed back in his chair, looking out the window and coughing. He reached into his pocket and handed something to me without looking around. It was a piece of chewing gum.

"Much obliged," I said. "Well, I reckon I might as well start back. I got a right fer piece to go."

"Wait," the soldier said. Then he telephoned again and I said again I better start back, and he said again, "Wait. Remember what Pete told you."

So we waited, and then another lady come in, old, too, in a fur coat, too, but she smelled all right, she never had no artermatic writing pen nor no case history neither. She come in and the soldier got up and she looked around quick until she saw me, and come and put her hand on my shoulder light and quick and easy as maw herself might 'a' done it.

"Come on," she said. "Let's go home to dinner."

"Nome," I said. "I got to ketch the bus to Jefferson."

"I know. There's plenty of time. We'll go home and eat dinner first."

She had a car. And now we was right down in the middle of all them other cars. We was almost under the busses, and all them crowds of people on the street close enough to where I could have talked to them if I had knowed who they was. After a while she stopped the car. "Here we are," she said, and I looked at it, and if all that was her house, she sho had a big family. But all of it wasn't. We crossed a hall with trees growing in it and went into a little room without nothing in it but a Negro dressed up in a uniform a heap shinier than them soldiers had, and the Negro shut the door, and then I hollered, "Look out!" and grabbed, but it was all right; that whole little room jest went right on up and stopped and the door opened and we was in another hall, and the lady unlocked a door and we went in, and there was another soldier, an old feller, with a britching strop, too, and a silver-colored bird on each shoulder.

"Here we are," the lady said. "This is Colonel McKellogg. Now, what would you like for dinner?"

"I reckon I'll jest have some ham and eggs and coffee," I said.

She had done started to pick up the telephone. She stopped. "Coffee?" she said, "When did you start drinking coffee?"

"I don't know," I said. "I reckon it was before I could remember."

"You're about eight, aren't you?" she said.

"Nome," I said. "I'm eight and ten months. Going on eleven months."

She telephoned then. Then we set there and I told them how Pete had jest left that morning for Pearl Harbor and I had aimed to go with him, but I would have to go back home to take care of maw and look after Pete's ten acres, and she said how they had a little boy about my size, too, in a school in the East. Then a Negro, another one, in a short kind of shirttail coat, rolled a kind of wheelbarrer in. It had my ham and eggs and a glass of milk and a piece of pie, too, and I thought I was hungry. But when I taken the first bite I found out I couldn't swallow it, and I got up quick.

"I got to go," I said.

"Wait," she said.

"I got to go," I said.

"Just a minute," she said. "I've already telephoned for the car. It won't be but a minute now. Can't you drink the milk even? Or maybe some of your coffee?"

"Nome," I said. "I ain't hungry. I'll eat when I git home." Then the telephone rung. She never even answered it.

"There," she said. "There's the car." And we went back down in that 'ere little moving room with the dressed-up Negro. This time it was a big car with a soldier driving it. I got into the front with him. She give the soldier a dollar. "He might get hungry," she said. "Try to find a decent place for him."

"O.K., Mrs. McKellogg," the soldier said.

Then we was gone again. And now I could see Memphis good, bright in the sunshine, while we was swinging around it. And the first thing I knowed, we was back on the same highway the bus run on this morning—the patches of stores and them big gins and sawmills, and Memphis running on for miles, it seemed like to me, before it begun to give out. Then we was running again between the fields and woods, running fast now, and except for that soldier, it was like I hadn't never been to Memphis a-tall. We was going fast now. At this rate, before I knowed it we would be home again, and I thought about me riding up to Frenchman's Bend in this here big car with a soldier running it, and all of a sudden I begun to cry. I never knowed I was fixing to, and I couldn't stop it. I set there by that soldier, crying. We was going fast.

About the author

William Faulkner (1897–   ) has spent most of his life in Mississippi, which is very often the locale of his novels. Born of an old Southern family, Faulkner is frequently concerned with the decline of the South from the aristocratic splendor of former days. His books are not easy to read for he often tells his stories through illiterate characters, and his style is marked by long, involved sentences. Still, the emotional power of his stories is very great. Many of these stories have been successfully adapted for both stage and screen. In 1950, Faulkner became the fourth American to be awarded the Nobel prize for literature.

Questions for discussion

1. Why did Pete feel that he had to go to war? Why did his little brother go off to Memphis to join the Army?
2. Pete said to his brother, "I expected to have more trouble with you than with all the rest of them put together." How did this turn out to be true? Why did Pete expect his brother to be troublesome?
3. Why did the people at the bus station help the boys get to Memphis? What were their impressions of him?
4. Even though the boy attacked one of the soldiers with a knife, everyone else in the Army office was kind to him. Why did they treat him with respect? Why didn't they ridicule him for wanting to join the Army?
5. Not many eight-year-old boys would run away from home and walk 22 miles in the night to join the Army. How does the author make the boy's action seem reasonable? Point out the details that show how close the brothers were to each other.
6. The boy accepts his brother's order to return home without arguing. Why does this seem to be a reasonable way for him to act?
7. It is difficult to portray moments of deep feeling in people's lives without being sentimental. The leave-taking of a loved-one who is going off to war is not a casual moment. The author avoids sentimentality by telling what people did, not what they thought. How did the mother and father behave at the leave-taking? How did Pete and the boy behave? Was the family showing its feelings or hiding them?
8. How did the leave-taking in Memphis differ from the one at home?
9. What foreshadowing of the next to the last sentence is there in the scene at the McKellogg home?
10. While the boy behaves like a grown-up, both in going to Memphis and then in returning home, he is also still a small boy seeing many new wonders for the first time. What does the last sentence show about the boy?
11. Throughout the story, humor arises from the country boy's way of looking at things. Point out examples of this. Can you identify the items that caught the boy's attention? The big house where Mrs. McKellogg lived? The little room that moved up and down? The wheelbarrow on which his dinner appeared?

Vocabulary growth

LEVELS OF USAGE. Faulkner uses three kinds of speech in this story: the boy's speech, the speech of his brother, and the speech of the lieutenant and the McKelloggs.

a. Show how they differ.

b. Where did the boy learn his kind of speech?

c. Why is Pete's speech different from that of his brother?

d. If the boy were actually telling the story and repeating the speeches of the lieutenant and Mrs. McKellogg in his own words, how would they have sounded? Why did the author represent the lieutenant and Mrs. McKellogg in their own kind of speech?

For composition

1. Write a paragraph to explain the title. Remember that the word *soldier* implies courage.

2. Make a list of the boy's personality traits as evidenced by his actions. Write a paragraph character sketch of the boy.

3. The story is written in the first person from the boy's point of view. To see how greatly this contributes to the story, try writing one scene in the first person from Pete's point of view. You might take the opening paragraphs for an example. You would begin, "My brother and I—"

4. What happened after the boy got home? What did he tell his parents? Write a narrative account of this scene. You might begin, "Ma was settin' on the porch when I got out of the car."

By the Waters of Babylon

STEPHEN VINCENT BENÉT

Here is the story of a young man's adventure into the unknown. Physical danger and even the threat of death could not stop him. As you read, you will be surprised to discover where and when the adventure begins.

THE north and the west and the south are good hunting ground, but it is forbidden to go east. It is forbidden to go to any of the Dead Places except to search for metal and then he who touches the metal must be a priest or the son of a priest. Afterwards, both the man and the metal must be purified. These are the rules and the laws; they are well made. It is forbidden to cross the great river and look upon the place that was the Place of the Gods—this is most strictly forbidden. We do not even say its name though we know its name. It is there that spirits live, and demons—it is there that there are the ashes of the Great Burning. These things are forbidden—they have been forbidden since the beginning of time.

My father is a priest; I am the son of a priest. I have been in the Dead Places near us, with my father—at first, I was afraid. When my father went into the house to search for the metal, I stood by the door and my heart felt small and weak. It was a dead man's house, a spirit house. It did not have the smell of man, though there were old bones in a corner. But it is not fitting that a priest's son should show fear. I looked at the bones in the shadow and kept my voice still.

Then my father came out with the metal—a good, strong piece. He looked at me with both eyes but I had not run away. He gave me the metal to hold—I took it and did not die. So he knew that I was truly his son and would be a priest in my time. That was when I was very young—nevertheless, my brothers would not have done it, though they are good hunters. After that, they gave me the good piece of meat and the warm corner by the fire. My father watched over me—he was glad that I should be a priest. But when I boasted or wept without a reason, he punished me more strictly than my brothers. That was right.

After a time, I myself was allowed to go into the dead houses and search for metal. So I learned the ways of those houses—and if I saw bones, I was no longer afraid. The bones are light and old—sometimes they will fall into dust if you touch them. But that is a great sin.

I was taught the chants and the spells—I was taught how to stop the running of blood from a wound and many secrets. A priest must know many secrets—that was what my father said. If the hunters think we do all things by chants and spells, they may believe so—it does not hurt them. I was taught how to read in the old books and how to make the old writings—that was hard and took a long time. My knowledge made me happy—it was like a fire in my heart. Most of all, I liked to hear of the Old Days and the stories of the gods. I asked myself many questions that I could not answer, but it was good to ask them. At night, I would lie awake and listen to the wind— it seemed to me that it was the voice of the gods as they flew through the air.

We are not ignorant like the Forest People—our women spin wool on the wheel, our priests wear a white robe. We do not eat grubs from the tree, we have not forgotten the old writings, although they are hard to understand. Nevertheless, my knowledge and my lack of knowledge burned in me—I wished to know more. When I was a man at last, I came to my father and said, "It is time for me to go on my journey. Give me your leave."

He looked at me for a long time, stroking his beard, then he said at last, "Yes. It is time." That night, in the house of the priest-hood, I asked for and received purification. My body hurt but my spirit was a cool stone. It was my father himself who questioned me about my dreams.

He bade me look into the smoke of the fire and see—I saw and told what I saw. It was what I have always seen—a river, and, beyond it, a great Dead Place and in it the gods walking. I have always thought about that. His eyes were stern when I told him—he was no longer my father but a priest. He said, "This is a strong dream."

"It is mine," I said, while the smoke waved and my head felt light. They were singing the Star song in the outer chamber and it was like the buzzing of bees in my head.

He asked me how the gods were dressed and I told him how they were dressed. We know how they were dressed from the book, but I saw them as if they were before me. When I had finished, he threw the sticks three times and studied them as they fell.

"This is a very strong dream," he said. "It may eat you up."

"I am not afraid," I said and looked at him with both eyes. My voice sounded thin in my ears but that was because of the smoke.

He touched me on the breast and the forehead. He gave me the bow and the three arrows.

"Take them," he said. "It is forbidden to travel east. It is forbidden to cross the river. It is forbidden to go to the Place of the Gods. All these things are forbidden."

"All these things are forbidden," I said, but it was my voice that spoke and not my spirit. He looked at me again.

"My son," he said. "Once I had young dreams. If your dreams do not eat you up, you may be a great priest. If they eat you, you are still my son. Now go on your journey."

I went fasting, as is the law. My body hurt but not my heart. When the dawn came, I was out of sight of the village. I prayed and purified myself, waiting for a sign. The sign was an eagle. It flew east.

Sometimes signs are sent by bad spirits. I waited again on the flat rock, fasting, taking no food. I was very still—I could feel the sky above me and the earth beneath. I waited till the sun was beginning to sink. Then three deer passed in the valley, going east—they did not wind me or see me. There was a white fawn with them—a very great sign.

I followed them, at a distance, waiting for what would happen. My heart was troubled about going east, yet I knew that I must go. My head hummed with my fasting—I did not even see the panther spring upon the white fawn. But, before I knew it, the bow was in my hand. I shouted and the panther lifted his head from the fawn. It is not easy to kill a panther with one arrow but the arrow went through his eye and into his brain. He died as he tried to spring— he rolled over, tearing at the ground. Then I knew I was meant to go east—I knew that was my journey. When the night came, I made my fire and roasted meat.

It is eight suns' journey to the east and a man passes by many Dead Places. The Forest People are afraid of them but I am not. Once I made my fire on the edge of a Dead Place at night and, next morning, in the dead house, I found a good knife, little rusted. That was small to what came afterward but it made my heart feel big. Always when I looked for game, it was in front of my arrow, and twice I passed hunting parties of the Forest People without their knowing. So I knew my magic was strong and my journey clean, in spite of the law.

Toward the setting of the eighth sun, I came to the banks of the great river. It was half-a-day's journey after I had left the god-road—we do not use the god-roads now for they are falling apart into great blocks of stone, and the forest is safer going. A long way off, I had seen the water through trees but the trees were thick. At last, I came out upon an open place at the top of a cliff. There was the great river below, like a giant in the sun. It is very long, very wide. It could eat all the streams we know and still be thirsty. Its name is Ou-dis-sun, the Sacred, the Long. No man of my tribe had seen it, not even my father, the priest. It was magic and I prayed.

Then I raised my eyes and looked south. It was there, the Place of the Gods.

How can I tell what it was like—you do not know. It was there, in the red light, and they were too big to be houses. It was there with the red light upon it, mighty and ruined. I knew that in another moment the gods would see me. I covered my eyes with my hands and crept back into the forest.

Surely, that was enough to do, and live. Surely it was enough to spend the night upon the cliff. The Forest People themselves do not come near. Yet, all through the night, I knew that I should have to cross the river and walk in the places of the gods, although the gods ate me up. My magic did not help me at all and yet there was a fire in my bowels, a fire in my mind. When the sun rose, I thought, "My journey has been clean. Now I will go home from my journey." But, even as I thought so, I knew I could not. If I went to the Place of the Gods, I would surely die, but, if I did not go, I could never be at peace with my spirit again. It is better to lose one's life than one's spirit, if one is a priest and the son of a priest.

Nevertheless, as I made the raft, the tears ran out of my eyes.

The Forest People could have killed me without fight, if they had come upon me then, but they did not come. When the raft was made, I said the sayings for the dead and painted myself for death. My heart was cold as a frog and my knees like water, but the burning in my mind would not let me have peace. As I pushed the raft from the shore, I began my death song—I had the right. It was a fine song.

"I am John, son of John," I sang. "My people are the Hill People.
    They are the men.
I go into the Dead Places but I am not slain.
I take the metal from the Dead Places but I am not blasted.
I travel upon the god-roads and am not afraid. E-yah! I have killed
    the panther, I have killed the fawn!
E-yah! I have come to the great river. No man has come there before.
It is forbidden to go east, but I have gone, forbidden to go on the
    great river, but I am there.
Open your hearts, you spirits, and hear my song.
    Now I go to the Place of the Gods, I shall not return.
My body is painted for death and my limbs weak, but my heart is big
    as I go to the Place of the Gods!"

All the same, when I came to the Place of the Gods, I was afraid, afraid. The current of the great river is very strong—it gripped my raft with its hands. That was magic, for the river itself is wide and calm. I could feel evil spirits about me, in the bright morning; I could feel their breath on my neck as I was swept down the stream. Never have I been so much alone—I tried to think of my knowledge, but it was a squirrel's heap of winter nuts. There was no strength in my knowledge any more and I felt small and naked as a new-hatched bird—alone upon the great river, the servant of the gods.

Yet, after a while, my eyes were opened and I saw. I saw both banks of the river—I saw that once there had been god-roads across it, though now they were broken and fallen like broken vines. Very great they were, and wonderful and broken—broken in the time of the Great Burning when the fire fell out of the sky. And always the current took me nearer to the Place of the Gods, and the huge ruins rose before my eyes.

I do not know the customs of rivers—we are the People of the Hills. I tried to guide my raft with the pole but it spun around. I thought the river meant to take me past the Place of the Gods and out into the Bitter Water of the legends. I grew angry then—my heart felt strong. I said aloud, "I am a priest and the son of a priest!" The gods heard me—they showed me how to paddle with the pole on one side of the raft. The current changed itself—I drew near to the Place of the Gods.

When I was very near, my raft struck and turned over. I can swim in our lakes—I swam to the shore. There was a great spike of rusted metal sticking out into the river—I hauled myself up upon it and sat there, panting. I had saved my bow and two arrows and the knife I found in the Dead Place but that was all. My raft went whirling downstream toward the Bitter Water. I looked after it, and thought if it had trod me under, at least I would be safely dead. Nevertheless, when I had dried my bowstring and re-strung it, I walked forward to the Place of the Gods.

It felt like ground underfoot; it did not burn me. It is not true what some of the tales say, that the ground there burns forever, for I have been there. Here and there were the marks and stains of the Great Burning, on the ruins, that is true. But they were old marks and old stains. It is not true either, what some of our priests say, that it is an island covered with fogs and enchantments. It is not. It is a great Dead Place—greater than any Dead Place we know. Everywhere in it there are god-roads, though most are cracked and broken. Everywhere there are the ruins of the high towers of the gods.

How shall I tell what I saw? I went carefully, my strung bow in my hand, my skin ready for danger. There should have been the wailings of spirits and the shrieks of demons, but there were not. It was very silent and sunny where I had landed—the wind and the rain and the birds that drop seeds had done their work—the grass grew in the cracks of the broken stone. It is a fair island—no wonder the gods built there. If I had come there, a god, I also would have built.

How shall I tell what I saw? The towers are not all broken—here and there one still stands, like a great tree in a forest, and the birds nest high. But the towers themselves look blind, for the gods are gone. I saw a fish-hawk, catching fish in the river. I saw a little dance of white butterflies over a great heap of broken stones and columns. I went there and looked about me—there was a carved stone with cut-letters, broken in half. I can read letters but I could not understand these. They said UBTREAS. There was also the shattered image of a man or a god. It had been made of white stone and he wore his hair tied back like a woman's. His name was ASHING, as I read on the cracked half of a stone. I thought it wise to pray to ASHING, though I do not know that god.

How shall I tell what I saw? There was no smell of man left, on stone or metal. Nor were there many trees in that wilderness of stone. There are many pigeons, nesting and dropping in the towers—the gods must have loved them, or, perhaps, they used them for sacrifices. There are wild cats that roam the god-roads, green-eyed, unafraid of man. At night they wail like demons but they are not demons. The wild dogs are more dangerous, for they hunt in a pack, but them I did not meet till later. Everywhere there are the carved stones, carved with magical numbers or words.

I went north—I did not try to hide myself. When a god or a demon saw me, then I would die, but meanwhile I was no longer afraid. My hunger for knowledge burned in me—there was so much that I could not understand. After awhile, I knew that my belly was hungry. I could have hunted for my meat, but I did not hunt. It is known that the gods did not hunt as we do—they got their food from enchanted boxes and jars. Sometimes these are still found in the Dead Places—once, when I was a child and foolish, I opened such a jar and tasted it and found the food sweet. But my father found out and punished me for it strictly, for, often, that food is death. Now, though, I had long gone past what was forbidden, and I entered the likeliest towers, looking for the food of the gods.

I found it at last in the ruins of a great temple in the mid-city. A mighty temple it must have been, for the roof was painted like the sky at night with its stars—that much I could see, though the colors were faint and dim. It went down into great caves and tunnels—perhaps they kept their slaves there. But when I started to climb down, I heard the squeaking of rats, so I did not go—rats are unclean, and there must have been many tribes of them, from the squeaking. But near there, I found food, in the heart of a ruin, behind a door that still opened. I ate only the fruits from the jars—they had a very sweet taste. There was drink, too, in bottles of glass—the drink of the gods was strong and made my head swim. After I had eaten and drunk, I slept on the top of a stone, my bow at my side.

When I woke, the sun was low. Looking down from where I lay,

I saw a dog sitting on his haunches. His tongue was hanging out of his mouth; he looked as if he were laughing. He was a big dog, with a gray-brown coat, as big as a wolf. I sprang up and shouted at him but he did not move—he just sat there as if he were laughing. I did not like that. When I reached for a stone to throw, he moved swiftly out of the way of the stone. He was not afraid of me; he looked at me as if I were meat. No doubt I could have killed him with an arrow, but I did not know if there were others. Moreover, night was falling.

I looked about me—not far away there was a great, broken god-road, leading north. The towers were high enough, but not so high, and while many of the dead-houses were wrecked, there were some that stood. I went toward this god-road, keeping to the heights of the ruins, while the dog followed. When I had reached the god-road, I saw that there were others behind him. If I had slept later, they would have come upon me asleep and torn out my throat. As it was, they were sure enough of me; they did not hurry. When I went into the dead-house, they kept watch at the entrance—doubtless they thought they would have a fine hunt. But a dog cannot open a door and I knew, from the books, that the gods did not like to live on the ground but on high.

I had just found a door I could open when the dogs decided to rush. Ha! They were surprised when I shut the door in their faces—it was a good door, of strong metal. I could hear their foolish baying beyond it but I did not stop to answer them. I was in darkness—I found stairs and climbed. There were many stairs, turning around till my head was dizzy. At the top was another door—I found the knob and opened it. I was in a long small chamber—on one side of it was a bronze door that could not be opened, for it had no handle. Perhaps there was a magic word to open it but I did not have the word. I turned to the door in the opposite side of the wall. The lock of it was broken and I opened it and went in.

Within, there was a place of great riches. The god who lived there must have been a powerful god. The first room was a small ante-room—I waited there for some time, telling the spirits of the place that I came in peace and not as a robber. When it seemed to me that they had had time to hear me, I went on. Ah, what riches! Few, even, of the windows had been broken—it was all as it had been. The great windows that looked over the city had not been broken at all though they were dusty and streaked with many years. There were coverings on the floors, the colors not greatly faded, and the chairs were soft and deep. There were pictures upon the walls, very strange, very wonderful—I remember one of a bunch of flowers in a jar—if you came close to it, you could see nothing but bits of color, but if you stood away from it, the flowers might have been picked yesterday. It made my heart feel strange to look at this picture—and to look at the figure of a bird, in some hard clay, on a table and see it so like our birds. Everywhere there were books and writings, many in tongues that I could not read. The god who lived there must have been a wise god and full of knowledge. I felt I had right there, as I sought knowledge also.

Nevertheless, it was strange. There was a washing-place but no water—perhaps the gods washed in air. There was a cooking-place but no wood, and though there was a machine to cook food, there was no place to put fire in it. Nor were there candles or lamps—there were things that looked like lamps but they had neither oil nor wick. All these things were magic, but I touched them and lived—the magic had gone out of them. Let me tell one thing to show. In the washing-place, a thing said "Hot" but it was not hot to the touch—another thing said "Cold" but it was not cold. This must have been a strong magic but the magic was gone. I do not understand—they had ways—I wish that I knew.

It was close and dry and dusty in their house of the gods. I have said the magic was gone but that is not true—it had gone from the magic things but it had not gone from the place. I felt the spirits about me, weighing upon me. Nor had I ever slept in a Dead Place before—and yet, tonight, I must sleep there. When I thought of it, my tongue felt dry in my throat, in spite of my wish for knowledge. Almost I would have gone down again and faced the dogs, but I did not.

I had not gone through all the rooms when the darkness fell. When it fell, I went back to the big room looking over the city and made fire. There was a place to make fire and a box with wood in it, though I do not think they cooked there. I wrapped myself in a floor-covering and slept in front of the fire—I was very tired.

Now I tell what is very strong magic. I woke in the midst of the night. When I woke, the fire had gone out and I was cold. It seemed to me that all around me there were whisperings and voices. I closed my eyes to shut them out. Some will say that I slept again, but I do not think that I slept. I could feel the spirits drawing my spirit out of my body as a fish is drawn on a line.

Why should I lie about it? I am a priest and the son of a priest. If there are spirits, as they say, in the small Dead Places near us, what spirits must there not be in that great Place of the Gods? And would not they wish to speak? After such long years? I know that I felt myself drawn as a fish is drawn on a line. I had stepped out of my body—I could see my body asleep in front of the cold fire, but it was not I. I was drawn to look out upon the city of the gods.

It should have been dark, for it was night, but it was not dark. Everywhere there were lights—lines of light—circles and blurs of light —ten thousand torches would not have been the same. The sky itself was alight—you could barely see the stars for the glow in the sky. I thought to myself "This is strong magic" and trembled. There was a roaring in my ears like the rushing of rivers. Then my eyes grew used to the light and my ears to the sound. I knew that I was seeing the city as it had been when the gods were alive.

That was a sight indeed—yes, that was a sight: I could not have seen it in the body—my body would have died. Everywhere went the gods, on foot and in chariots—there were gods beyond number and counting and their chariots blocked the streets. They had turned night to day for their pleasure—they did not sleep with the sun. The noise of their coming and going was the noise of many waters. It was magic what they could do—it was magic what they did.

I looked out of another window—the great vines of their bridges were mended and the god-roads went east and west. Restless, restless, were the gods and always in motion! They burrowed tunnels under rivers—they flew in the air. With unbelievable tools they did giant works—no part of the earth was safe from them, for, if they wished for a thing, they summoned it from the other side of the world. And always, as they labored and rested, as they feasted and made love, there was a drum in their ears—the pulse of the giant city, beating and beating like a man's heart.

Were they happy? What is happiness to the gods? They were great, they were mighty, they were wonderful and terrible. As I looked upon them and their magic, I felt like a child—but a little more, it seemed to me, and they would pull down the moon from the sky. I saw them with wisdom beyond wisdom and knowledge beyond knowledge. And yet not all they did was well done—even I could see that—and yet their wisdom could not but grow until all was peace.

Then I saw their fate come upon them and that was terrible past speech. It came upon them as they walked the streets of their city. I have been in the fights with the Forest People—I have seen men die. But this was not like that. When gods war with gods, they use weapons we do not know. It was fire falling out of the sky and a mist that poisoned. It was the time of the Great Burning and the Destruction. They ran about like ants in the streets of their city—poor gods, poor gods! Then the towers began to fall. A few escaped—yes, a few. The legends tell it. But, even after the city had become a Dead Place, for many years the poison was still in the ground. I saw it happen, I saw the last of them die. It was darkness over the broken city and I wept.

All this, I saw. I saw it as I have told it, though not in the body. When I woke in the morning, I was hungry, but I did not think first of my hunger for my heart was perplexed and confused. I knew the reason for the Dead Places but I did not see why it had happened. It seemed to me it should not have happened, with all the magic they had. I went through the house looking for an answer. There was so much in the house I could not understand—and yet I am a priest and the son of a priest. It was like being on one side of the great river, at night, with no light to show the way.

Then I saw the dead god. He was sitting in his chair, by the window, in a room I had not entered before and, for the first moment, I thought that he was alive. Then I saw the skin on the back of his hand—it was like dry leather. The room was shut, hot and dry—no doubt that had kept him as he was. At first I was afraid to approach him—then the fear left me. He was sitting looking out over the city—he was dressed in the clothes of the gods. His age was neither young nor old—I could not tell his age. But there was wisdom in his face and great sadness. You could see that he would have not run away. He had sat at his window, watching his city die—then he himself had died. But it is better to lose one's life than one's spirit—and you could see from the face that his spirit had not been lost. I knew, that, if I touched him, he would fall into dust—and yet, there was something unconquered in the face.

That is all of my story, for then I knew he was a man—I knew then that they had been men, neither gods nor demons. It is a great knowledge, hard to tell and believe. They were men—they went a dark road, but they were men. I had no fear after that—I had no fear going home, though twice I fought off the dogs and once I was hunted for two days by the Forest People. When I saw my father again, I prayed and was purified. He touched my lips and my breast, he said, "You went away a boy. You come back a man and a priest." I said, "Father, they were men! I have been in the Place of the Gods and seen it! Now slay me, if it is the law—but still I know they were men."

He looked at me out of both eyes. He said, "The law is not always the same shape—you have done what you have done. I could not have done it my time, but you come after me. Tell!"

I told and he listened. After that, I wished to tell all the people but he showed me otherwise. He said, "Truth is a hard deer to hunt. If you eat too much truth at once, you may die of the truth. It was not idly that our fathers forbade the Dead Places." He was right—it is better the truth should come little by little. I have learned that, being a priest. Perhaps, in the old days, they ate knowledge too fast.

Nevertheless, we make a beginning. It is not for the metal alone we go to the Dead Places now—there are the books and the writings. They are hard to learn. And the magic tools are broken—but we can look at them and wonder. At least, we make a beginning. And, when I am chief priest we shall go beyond the great river. We shall go to the Place of the Gods—the place newyork—not one man but a company. We shall look for the images of the gods and find the god ASHING and the others—the gods Lincoln and Baltimore and Moses. But they were men who built the city, not gods or demons. They were men. I remember the dead man's face. They were men who were here before us. We must build again.

About the author

Stephen Vincent Benét (1898–1943) began writing in his youth and had already published a volume of verse before he entered Yale. He is equally celebrated as a short story writer and as a poet. His great poem of the Civil War, *John Brown's Body*, won for him a Pulitzer Prize. "The Devil and Daniel Webster" ranks among the all-time favorite American short stories, and has been made into a motion picture, a one-act play, and an opera. In his final years, Benét wrote radio plays on patriotic themes to rally support for America's cause in World War II.

Questions for discussion

1. The priest's son broke the law of his tribe, but in the end he was not punished. Were his actions the same kind of crimes as robbery or murder?

2. What punishment did the youth face for breaking the law? Why was he not punished? Should he have been? Why?

3. What did the priest mean when he said, "The law is not always the same shape."?

4. What is the difference between questioning authority and defying authority? Was the priest's son defiant, or was he merely questioning? How does the priest's son feel at the close of the story?

5. The priest's son was willing to suffer the penalty for breaking the law in order to get what he wanted. What was it that he wanted? What were his reasons for going toward the forbidden East?

6. FLASHBACK. A flashback is an interruption in the continuity of a story. The writer uses the flashback in order to point up some important past event that the reader must know about if he is to fully understand the story. If you will remember, flashback was used in "Molly Morgan." What purpose did it serve? Can you find flashbacks in "By the Waters of Babylon"? What purpose do they serve in this story?

7. The youth, facing new things and new situations, could explain them only in terms of what he knew. Compare his experiences and his explanations of them with those of the boy in "Two Soldiers." How are they alike?

8. What was the great shattering discovery that the priest's son made? Did he admire the ways of the gods? What is his explanation of their destruction?

9. PLOT. In many stories there is a strong conflict between a hero (the protagonist) and an opponent (the antagonist). In some stories the conflict is between the protagonist and external forces as in "The Sea Devil." There are physical obstacles that the hero must overcome in order to attain his goal. Sometimes the conflict is internal conflict that takes place within the mind and heart of the hero. In "By the Waters of Babylon," there is an external conflict between the priest's son and physical dangers. But he also meets and overcomes an obstacle within himself. What physical obstacles does the priest's son meet? Within himself, what inner obstacles, thoughts and feelings did he have to overcome? One side of this conflict was his desire for

knowledge. What was the other side? At what point in the story has he finally overcome the inner obstacles?

10. When the young man himself became a priest, he followed his father's advice not to tell his people all about his discovery right away. Why? What is the main underlying idea or theme of this story?

Vocabulary growth

VARIANT MEANINGS. Most words in common use have more than one meaning. Some of them like *law* have many meanings. The laws of a country are passed by people in power—dictators, kings, elected councils, legislatures, and so on. They are interpreted by courts and enforced by police, marshals, and in some countries by soldiers.

But there are other kinds of law. What is moral law, for example? Who enforces it? What is an economic law? What makes it work? What is a law of physics or chemistry? All of these kinds of law have something in common. What is it? Your dictionary will help you.

For composition

1. This story raises the troublesome question of how to behave towards authority. You might think through some of the questions below and write a statement of your views on "Young People and Authorities."
   a. What authorities are there besides the law?
   b. What would happen if no one ever questioned authorities?
   c. What is the difference between questioning and defying authority?
   d. What would happen if everyone decided for himself which laws he would obey and which he would break?
2. What would happen in your community if a bomb fell upon it? Write a narrative with the title "When the Bomb Fell."
3. You are one of the Hill People. Write the story of the return of the priest's son, and tell what he said. Read the last two pages of the story carefully before beginning.